Performance Assessment

IN THE SCIENCE CLASSROOM

Glencoe Professional Science Series

Glencoe McGraw-Hill

New York, New York Columbus, Ohio Woodland Hills, California Peoria, Illinois

Glencoe/McGraw-Hill
*A Division of The **McGraw-Hill** Companies*

Send all inquiries to:
Glencoe/McGraw-Hill
8787 Orion Place
Columbus, OH 43240

ISBN 0-07-825453-1
Printed in the United States of America
15 16 17 18 009 10 09 08

Table of Contents

Assessment in Today's Classroom

In This Section

- National standards and performance assessment, *p. 1*
- Authentic assessment and performance assessment, *p. 2*
- Assessment outcomes, *p. 3*
- Partnering with paper-and-pencil testing, *p. 3*

Assessing student performance in science without first understanding the goals of science education is a bit like trying to judge an Olympic event without first knowing any of the judging criteria. Since 1985, a major effort has been underway to redefine goals and promote reforms to K-12 science education. Project 2061, the long-term initiative of the American Association for the Advancement of Science, recognizes that students will witness a multitude of scientific and technological changes in the twenty-first century. To prepare them for these challenges, it developed a set of guidelines and standards to improve science, mathematics, and technology literacy.

Project 2061 recognizes that to make sense of our world students will need to think critically and independently, recognize and weigh alternative explanations of events, design trade-offs, and deal sensibly with problems that involve evidence, numbers, patterns, logical arguments, and uncertainties.

National Science Goals

National science standards help define the science that all students hould come to understand. Science education should provide students with the tools to:

- inquire
- know and understand scientific facts, concepts, principles, laws, and theories
- reason scientifically
- incorporate science in making personal decisions and taking positions on social issues
- communicate effectively about science

The fundamental facts and concepts of life, physical, and earth sciences are still essential to learning science. However, sequencing and connecting concepts within science and across the curriculum also are necessary skills. In addition, students should integrate basic and higher-level science process skills with conceptual knowledge. Such complex behaviors help students acquire higher-order thinking and problem-solving skills; skills that will prepare students to live in the twenty-first century's ever-changing society.

Assessment standards provide the criteria needed to judge progress toward the science education vision of "science for all." These standards can be used equally in the assessment of students, teachers, and programs. The assessment of student work should include both a study of a final product, such as a poster or a research report, and the processes that lead to them, such as descriptive journals or science logs.

Defining Assessment

Assessment is the day-to-day evaluation of your students in the classroom. To make meaningful assessments, information needs to be collected from students in a variety of forms. Traditional paper-and pencil tests are useful in measuring a student's knowledge about a particular subject or process. Alternative assessment encompasses assessment methods that do not fall into the paper-and-pencil testing category.

Alternative Assessment

Alternative assessment focuses on measuring procedural knowledge. It includes an enormous range of procedures used to gather information about what a student knows, believes, and can do. It focuses on individual student growth over time and emphasizes student strengths. Consideration is given to individual learning styles and skill level.

Many types of assessment fall under the umbrella of alternative assessment:

Authentic Assessment

Authentic assessment engages students in real-world situations. It presents authentic problem-solving tasks that students might encounter inside or outside of school. Further, it engages students in inquiry and projects that they care about. Examples of authentic assessment might include everyday observations in the classroom, independent projects, or tasks such as filling out job applications, writing letters to a corporation or politician, or analyzing a television commercial.

Performance Assessment

Performance assessment measures a student's performance in creating a particular product or exhibiting information. It can help in measuring content knowledge but it also incorporates higher-order thinking and processing. Performance assessment allows student to apply their knowledge to a specific problem or goal and can link to other content areas. Unlike traditional testing, it allows feedback during the process at various stages. This booklet focuses primarily on performance assessment and the tools available for measuring it effectively.

A performance task can be broken down into a process that requires the following action skills:

Step in Process	Thinking Skills Used
Getting the information	find, complete, count, collect, read, listen, define, describe, identify, list, match, name, observe (using all the senses),record, recite, select, scan
Working with the information	compare, contrast, classify, sort, distinguish, explain why, infer, sequence, analyze, synthesize, generalize, evaluate, make analogies, make models, and/or reason
Judging the quality of information	evaluate whether the information source is likely to be biased or objective, evaluate whether the information itself is accurate and complete
Using the information for a purpose	inform, persuade, motivate, entertain
Using information to craft a product/ presentation	speaking, debating, singing, writing, surveying, designing, drawing, computing, constructing, demonstrating, acting-out

Goals of Assessment

Plan and choose your tasks carefully. The outcomes of your assessment should allow you to:

- gauge each student's level of scientific reasoning
- improve student ability to apply scientific knowledge and reasoning
- improve student ability to communicate effectively about science

- identify student learning styles, as well as individual strengths and weaknesses
- identify areas of instruction that need more or less emphasis
- promote self- and peer assessment
- promote independent learning
- promote authentic learning

Partner with Traditional Testing

Traditional testing provides paper evidence. Such testing consists of multiple choice, true/false, matching, and short-answer questions that result in a curriculum based on facts and basic skills. In contrast, performance assessment gives a window on how well students use one or more elements of literacy.

Each teacher must find the proper balance of traditional testing and performance assessment. Sometimes traditional testing can be used first to ensure that your students have enough accurate information before performance assessment is used. And, sometimes performance assessment can be used first as a strategy to engage students in learning.

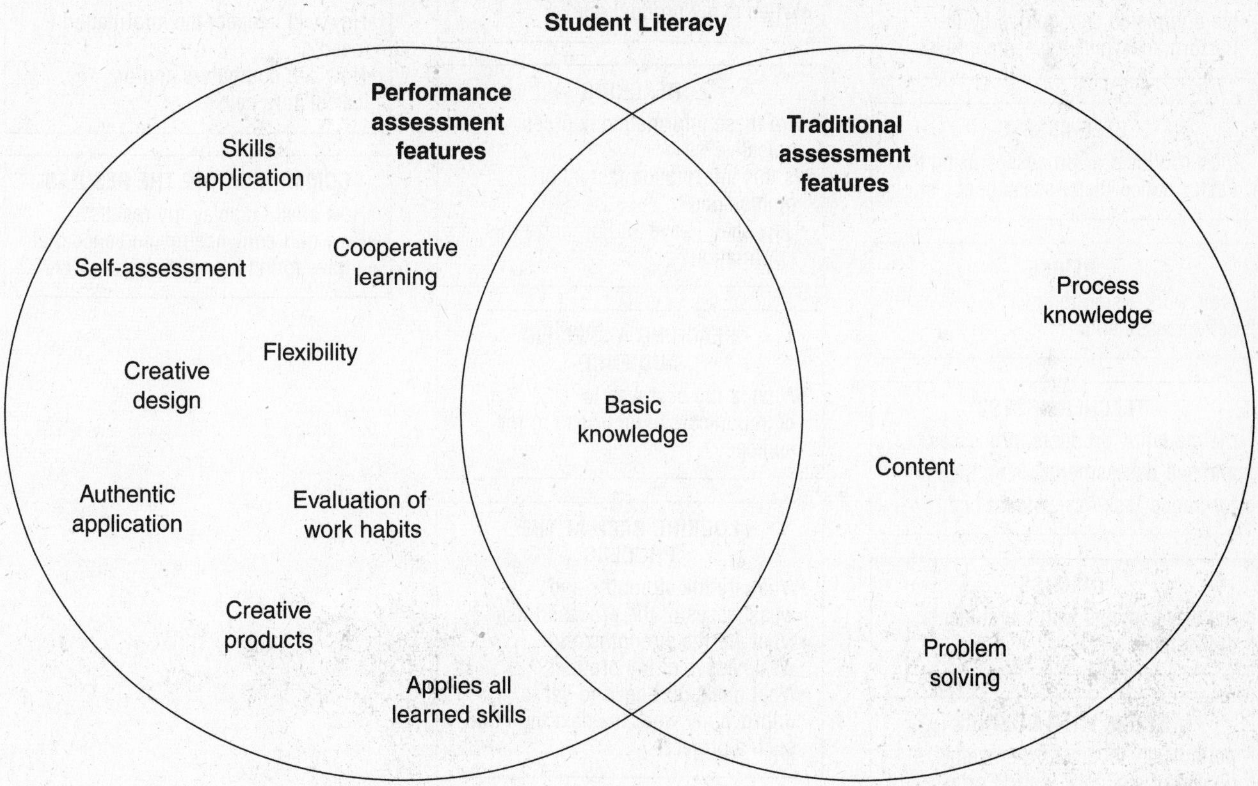

HOW CAN THIS SYSTEM BE IMPLEMENTED

SELECT
an appropriate Performance Task Assessment List of the product or process to be assessed in the students' tasks.

MODEL
through discussion and showing of excellent work which are similar to but not the same as the current task. Relate elements of these models to the elements listed on the Performance Task Assessment List.

PRODUCE
the completed task guided by the Performance Task Assessment List.

SELF-ASSESS
their products or processes using the Performance Task Assessment List.

REVISE
their work, using their self-assessments.

TEACHER ASSESS
the students' products, processes, and self-assessments using the Performance Task Assessment List.

DISCUSS
the assessments with the students individually.

SCORE WITH RUBRICS
periodically to assess the overall quality of students' work. Performance Task Assessment Lists may be used in assigning and explaining the Rubric scores.

FINDING AND USING INFORMATION

UNDERSTANDING THE TASK
- What is a reasonable topic?
- Who is the audience for my product?
- What kind of product will I make?
- What effect do I want my product to have on my audience?

SURVEYING WHAT I KNOW AND WHAT I NEED TO FIND OUT
- What do I really know about this topic?
- What do I know about my audience?
- What do I need to find out?
- Where and how will I get this information?
- When is my product due?

REACHING
- Are these information sources objective?
- Is this information factual or opinionated?
- How shall I save and organize this information?

REACHING A SPECIFIC AUDIENCE
- What is the best way to communicate my purpose to my audience?

LOOKING BACK AT THE PROCESS
- What are the strengths and weaknesses of the process I used?
- What are the strengths and weaknesses of my product?
- What goals do I need to set to improve my work the next time I do such a project?

USING MATHEMATICS TO SOLVE PROBLEMS

IDENTIFYING THE PROBLEM
- What part of this problem can I use math to solve?

UNDERSTANDING THE PROBLEM
- What exactly am I trying to solve?
- What do I really know?

FINDING NEEDED INFORMATION
- What information do I need to find?
- Where will I find it?

DECIDING ON THE TOOLS TO USE
- How will I collect the information I need?
- How can computers and/or calculators help?

COMMUNICATING THE RESULTS
- How shall I display my results?
- How do I convince my audience that I have found a reasonable answer?

Performance Assessment Toolbox

In This Section

- Using questioning to evaluate student performance, *p. 5*
- Learning to ask open-ended questions, *p. 5*
- Sample questions, *p. 7*
- Sample observation forms, *p. 9*

Tools vary for judging the performance of a task. Remember, your choice of assessment should be consistent with what you want to measure and infer. This section will give you ideas about different assessment tools, along with worksheets that you can use to evaluate those tools.

Observation and Questioning

Description

The assessment techniques of observation and questioning are not new to teachers of science. In every science classroom, students' behavior and performance on scientific tasks are observed and students are questioned about their work. During the introduction to a new topic or a review of previously taught material, teachers use questions to check student understanding and then make appropriate adjustments in their instructional approach.

The emerging process goals of science instruction, however, imply that the techniques of observation and questioning be re-examined to make sure they are being used effectively to assess the new goals. In other words, new curriculum standards require new or revised assessment methods.

How can you evaluate student performance on laboratory skills or probe critical-thinking and problem-solving tasks? How do you assess a student's knowledge of scientific connections? Read on for answers to these questions.

Problem Solving

First, let's look at problem solving. Traditionally, you assign students science problems to solve and then grade their written work on the basis of a right or wrong answer. This procedure has serious shortcomings and often reveals little useful information. For example, a student may understand how to solve a problem, but a misconception resulting in a wrong answer would lead you to think otherwise. A more powerful way to assess problem-solving competence is to ask students questions about how they tried to solve a problem. Listening to the student's descriptions of their thinking and observing their written work provides a more accurate assessment of problem-solving skills than simply grading answers on tests.

Thinking, Communicating, and Making Connections

Questioning students in a problem-solving context reveals not only how they think, but also their ability to communicate ideas clearly. You observe by listening, asking questions, and evaluating responses. Such a procedure allows you to change the direction of the questions to pursue other ideas or thoughts the students may have expressed, thus getting a fuller and deeper understanding of the process being evaluated. Asking the right questions also can reveal how students make connections about what they know.

Using Open-Ended Questions

Open-ended questions are the best type of questions to ask students to assess their knowledge of science processes. Such questions do not have a single answer. They allow students an opportunity to think for themselves and to demonstrate their understanding of a problem or other situation. The use of open-ended questions can reveal a great deal of interesting information about what students know and understand. They also allow students to express their originality and creativity. Open-ended questions are incompatible with the erroneous notion that science consists of memorizing responses to questions that always have one right answer. Open-ended questions teach students to see and understand science as a beautiful, logical, and connected body of ideas that has great practical significance in understanding the world in which we live.

Examples of Open-Ended Questions

Open-ended questions often involve the use of words such as:

- Describe
- Explain
- Compare
- Tell
- Analyze
- Examine
- Show
- Demonstrate
- Sketch
- Explore
- Illustrate
- Present
- Contrast
- Express
- Investigate
- Prove
- Restate
- Model
- Predict
- Define operationally

At various grade levels, you can say to students:

How would you explain . . . ?
Analyze the variables . . .
Tell the class why . . .

Observing Student Performances

Students can be observed working as individuals, in small groups, or within a class setting. Observations are useful for individual diagnostic purposes to determine what a student understands (so remedial action can be taken), to guide students working in a small group toward the goals of the group, or for instructional feedback as students participate in class instruction. Use the feedback you receive to modify instruction as it is taking place. That way, you'll be able to better meet the needs of the class.

Observation of students at work is a natural part of the classroom process. Very often, these informal observations are unplanned and no attempts are made to record what has been observed. However, to understand how a student solves problems, you should observe closely student attempts to solve problems. Only then will you be able to see how well students perform against standards.

The same is true for evaluating critical-thinking skills. This can be done by listening to students explain their reasons for their work. Observe their minds at work through the use of their language. Of course, written work also can help you form a complete picture of scientific competence.

Observations are useful in assessing performance in the following areas:

- Laboratory skills
- Problem-solving approaches
- Thinking processes
- Understanding concepts
- Communication skills
- Small group interaction
- Making connections

Implementing Questions

Questions, like observations, are an integral part of the instruction process. In fact, worthwhile observations often are the result of asking the right question. Questions can be directed toward individual students, small groups, or the class itself. Students' responses can be used for assessment purposes, to guide instruction, or to identify problems.

Sample Questions

Let's look at some sample questions as they relate to problem solving, laboratory skills, reasoning, and making connections.

Problem Solving

- Would you explain the problem in your own words?
- What is the problem about?
- Would making a drawing or a sketch be helpful in solving the problem?
- Explain the steps you would follow to solve the problem.

Laboratory Skills

- How could we test that idea?
- What variable will change our results?
- Write a short paragraph about the activity that you did in class today.
- Explain your solution to the problem at the chalkboard.

Reasoning

- Can you formulate a hypothesis based on the facts you know?
- Explain why the solution to the problem is incorrect
- Why are definitions necessary in science?
- Can you generalize that result?
- What conclusions can you draw about the hypothesis from the given data?

Making Connections

- Can you give a practical example of the use of that concept?
- How does water speed affect organisms in a stream?
- Why is the freezing and melting of water important in geology?
- What is the connection between pollution and quality of life?
- How would you graph the data from the experiment?
- Do you see any relationship of that idea to what we discussed yesterday?

Assessment Questions

When using questions to make an assessment of what a student knows, here are some general guidelines to follow:

1. Make a list of questions in advance.
2. Allow students sufficient time to answer your questions.
3. Encourage students to make notes and ask questions to clarify a point.
4. Record responses in an organized format.
5. Draw a conclusion about student responses.

Questions to Guide Instruction

During the course of an instructional period, that is, when you are developing a new topic, timely and astute questions can provide significant feedback as to how well the instruction is being received. Do the students understand the main points of the presentation? Are more examples needed? Should a review be introduced to reinforce ideas and skills from previous lessons? You need to know answers to these questions and others in order to shape the instruction to the class. Without asking questions, there is no way to find out where the students are. Effective science instruction and the use of good questions go hand-in-hand.

Questions for Error Analysis

One of the best ways to find out why students make certain types of errors is to ask them to explain their work. Usually, students' explanations reveal a faulty understanding of some key concept or a lack of knowledge of a specific fact or procedure.

Evaluation Methods

One of the major purposes of assessing student work is to provide feedback regarding how well they are doing. Students need to know what you think about their progress—or lack of it. Informal assessment methods, such as observations and questioning, are seldom documented, but they should be if feedback is to be accurate and effective.

Given the dynamics of a science classroom and the number of students you work with each day, methods of recording observations and the results of systematic questioning must be simple and easy to implement. Also, only *significant events* should be recorded. Such an event is likely to be either an atypical student behavior or a clear indication of some understanding or lack of it. Here are three methods that can be used to record significant events:

1. Make a *class list* of your students with a column for writing comments. Or use an *observation sheet* for each student.
2. Develop *profiles* for students. Each profile can evaluate important attributes, such as student's use of problem-solving strategies, scientific vocabulary, plausible arguments, or different models.
3. For each student, construct a *checklist* of skills, behaviors, or attributes that you want to encourage.

An example of such a checklist for assessing specific laboratory skills follows.

Laboratory Skills Assessment

Name ______________________ Date ____________

Rating scale:
1. student is careless **2.** student needs to improve **3.** student is proficient

Skill	Proficiency		
lights burner correctly	1	2	3
adjusts air and gas supplies correctly	1	2	3
decants correctly using a stirring rod	1	2	3
folds filter paper correctly	1	2	3
carries a balance correctly	1	2	3
determines mass accurately	1	2	3
positions thermometer correctly	1	2	3
records accurate reading	1	2	3
identifies the parts of a microscope	1	2	3
carries microscope correctly	1	2	3
focuses microscope correctly	1	2	3
inserts glass tubing correctly	1	2	3

A few suggestions for constructing and using a checklist:

- Focus on only a few students each day, perhaps four or five.
- Observe laboratory groups as a whole and as individuals.
- Document individual and group work.
- Use the list periodically, not daily.
- Have students review the initial list and make suggestions for revisions.
- Ask students to evaluate themselves, using the checklist.
- Leave space for notes.

Each evaluation method is a way of recording information about a student in order to provide feedback. Such feedback can take the form of written or oral comments by the teacher. Feedback provides a link with previous instruction, points the way to future instruction, and it tells students what learning outcomes you value. Feedback equips students to monitor their own progress and work toward the goals you established.

Sample Forms

Forms that can be used to record information resulting from observation and questioning.

Observation Sheet

Name ____________________

Date	Activity	Observed behavior

Name ____________ Week ______
Profile Notes

Class List

Name	Significant event	Action	
		Required	Taken

Presentations and Discussions

In This Section

- Using presentations in performance assessment, *p. 10*
- Topic ideas source list, *p. 11*
- How and why to document scientific growth, *p. 12*
- Sample observation forms, *p. 14–15*

Using Presentations

The use of student presentations and discussions can be a valuable tool in assessing student performance. Student presentations can involve oral presentations to the class or to small groups. They can be rather simple, such as explaining observations, or somewhat more involved, such as giving an oral report to the class. Student presentations also can involve the use of models to illustrate concepts and laboratory procedures, or the construction of bulletin board displays for the classroom. Student demonstrations of activities or safe use of scientific apparatus also are of value.

Using Discussions

Discussions involve small groups of students working together and can be teacher- or student-directed. In science classrooms, some students often are reluctant to participate because of fear of giving the wrong answer. As students learn science within a problem-solving context, the one-answer syndrome begins to dissipate and they start to open up and express their ideas more freely. Also, as students grow in their ability to solve problems and think scientifically, their self-confidence grows. A self-confident student is not afraid to discuss ideas with classmates.

An ideal way to motivate student discussions is through the use of cooperative learning groups. Students who might feel shy speaking in front of the whole class may be more at ease talking to a small group. Students also are less fearful of making errors when working with only two or three other students.

Why Are Presentations and Discussions Important?

What better way to assess a student's ability to communicate scientifically (and to find out what a student thinks) than to hear that student give a verbal explanation to a problem or an oral report on a topic of interest in science. Certainly, no written test could accomplish this.

How Can Presentations and Discussions Be Used in the Classroom?

The use of presentations and discussions must be a planned part of the instructional process. Explain to students that at certain times oral presentations will be part of the course work. Also, if students have never worked in cooperative learning groups before, they will need to be prepared for this experience. Another book in the Glencoe Science Professional Series, *Cooperative Learning in the Science Classroom,* may be helpful.

When students are asked to give a formal report or a presentation on a special topic, reach an agreement with the student regarding the topic. Topics should be chosen that support both content and process goals of science instruction. Some students may need guidance in selecting a topic, but the topic should never be imposed by you; that could dissolve the student's motivation to research the topic and present it.

Small group discussions should have a focus. Have students engage in problem-solving activities. Different strategies can be discussed, solutions can be checked and compared with those of other groups, and group presentations of solutions can be given to the entire class. Alternative methods of solving a problem can be discussed, and models and diagrams can be used to demonstrate solutions.

Students working cooperatively on long-term scientific projects should maintain a simplified log. The log can include written entries, such as their plan for conducting an experiment, the experiment data, and its analysis. In a six-week project, there may be three or four separate or related experiments. The log can be used as a basis for a reflective project report.

Suggestions for Presentations

Almost any topic that falls within the scientific maturity level of a student and the content of the course is a good one for a class presentation. The following list is a source of ideas for general categories of topics:

- solution to a scientific problem
- historical topic, person, or event
- extension of textbook topic
- enrichment topic
- experimental topic
- practical application topic
- calculator or computer topic
- scientific connection topic
- scientific logic topic
- famous living scientist
- famous theory or hypothesis
- major branches of science
- scientific notation
- multicultural topic

Sugestions for Small Group Discussions

Student work in small groups should be focused upon specific tasks. The discussions should be task-oriented, such as how to design and conduct an experiment. The following suggested activities are appropriate for small group work and discussion:

- solving problems within areas of science and engineering
- formulating problems
- solving applications related to other disciplines or the real world
- analyzing data to support or refute theories
- using models to learn concepts or do experiments
- discussing solutions to homework problems
- classifying objects, interpreting results, generating solutions, making graphs
- making and testing hypotheses
- planning group presentations
- using calculators or computers

When to Implement

Presentations and discussions can be used throughout the school year. Instruction and assessment need to work together to be successful. Presentations and discussions are tools for instruction that can be integrated into your teaching at any time.

How to Evaluate

The major goal of evaluating student presentations and discussions is to document student growth in understanding. Your key task is to isolate significant information about each student so that it can be documented. Trying to record everything students say or do is impossible and would provide no useful data anyway.

Identifying Areas of Growth

At the beginning of each school year, you need to know where each student is in order to identify and record areas of growth. Once a baseline has been established, you can readily observe and record student growth.

Growth in Problem Solving

Look for growth in the following areas:

- use of problem-solving strategies to understand and solve problems
- use of scientific models to identify key aspects of a situation in order to formulate a problem
- use of answers and results to problems and other scientific situations to verify and interpret them with respect to the original problem
- generalization of strategies and solutions to new problem situations
- use of problem-solving methods as a means of learning and understanding new content
- application of scientific modeling to real-world problems

Growth of Communication

Growth in these areas is significant:

- use of scientific vocabulary to explain ideas to others
- use of correct statements of definitions, laws, and theories
- use of definitions, laws, and theories to discuss, interpret, and evaluate scientific ideas
- use of scientific terms to make convincing arguments
- use of language to formulate problems, definitions, and generalizations discovered through investigations
- asking clear and concise questions and giving specific answers

Growth in Reasoning

Significant growth areas are as follows:

- use of deductive and inductive reasoning
- use of data-based arguments
- evaluation of their own thinking and of others' arguments
- making and testing hypotheses
- formulating data-based generalizations
- following logical arguments
- construction of scientific models
- appreciation of the use and power of logical reasoning in science

Documenting and Reporting Growth in Understanding

One way to document and report growth in understanding the process goals of science is by using a *checklist.* A checklist can be constructed using the areas of growth previously identified. A checklist should not be a burden but should make it easy for you to collect and record data about students.

A few suggestions for constructing and using a checklist follow. Remember, a checklist should be helpful and not be a burden to use.

- Focus on only a few students each day, perhaps four or five.
- Observe laboratory groups as a whole and as individuals.
- Document individual and group work.
- Use the list periodically, not daily.
- Have students review the initial list and make suggestions for revisions.
- Ask students to evaluate themselves using the checklist.
- Leave space for notes.

Each evaluation method is a way of recording information about a student in order to provide feedback. Such feedback can take the form of written or oral comments by you. Feedback provides a link with previous instruction, points the way to future instruction, and it tells students what learning outcomes you value. Feedback equips students to monitor their own progress and work toward the goals you established.

Name ______________________________

Growth Checklist

Connections	**Growth**	**Some growth**	**Needs work**
Use of concepts and process skills to explore and solve problems			
Use of one or more scientific ideas to understand other scientific ideas			
Use of science to solve problems in the real world or in other disciplines			
Recognition of equivalent representations to explore and solve problems			
Looking for and identifying connections within science			

Another way for a teacher to evaluate student presentations and discussions is to keep a record of significant understandings in the form of an *anecdotal report.* The compilation of such anecdotes can be used to track student performance and to review and write summary statements. Anecdotal reports consisting of brief comments are easy to implement and can be used over time as a reservoir of data for more comprehensive reports.

Anecdotal Report

Name: ______________________________

Comments

Date: ____________ ____________________

____
____
____
____
____

Date: ____________ ____________________

____
____
____
____
____

Date: ____________ ____________________

____
____
____
____
____

A *descriptive report* also can be helpful to document and report growth in scientific understanding. Such a report will take time to write, but it can be a very effective tool in evaluating a student's progress in science. The goals of a report are to point out what the student has done well and what areas need improvement. Here are some items that can be discussed in a descriptive report.

- the work a student has done
- examples of significant scientific events
- growth or improvement in a student's work
- areas that need additional work
- participation in class and small groups
- attitude toward science
- specific suggestions for additional work

Report of Performance

Name ____________________

Time period ____________________

Class ____________________

Description of work ____________________

____

____

Examples of significant work ____________________

____

____

Growth and improvement observed ____________________

____

____

Areas needing additional work ____________________

____

____

Group work ____________________

____

____

Attitude ____________________

____

____

Summary comments ____________________

____

____

Projects and Investigations

In This Section

- Using projects and investigations to connect to the real world, *p. 16*
- Getting students started, *p. 17*
- Suggested point values for analytical scoring, *p. 19*

Description

Projects and investigations can involve individual students or small groups of two to four students working cooperatively. They should be long-term assignments and include a wide variety of concepts, basic and integrated process skills, problem identification, and solution techniques. Students involved in an ongoing task should be involved for at least two to three weeks.

Projects involving more substantial activities can last a month or two. Since students should be involved in more than a few projects during the course of a school year, the ideal duration of a project is about four to five weeks.

Ideas for Projects and Investigations

Projects are a wonderful way to involve students in extended problem-solving situations. These situations may be purely scientific, but most likely will be related to the real world or to other disciplines. Projects can involve students in open-ended situations that may have a variety of acceptable results. Or, they may be of such a nature that the problem situation leads students to formulate questions or hypotheses that require further investigation. Projects also provide opportunities for students to explore scientific ideas using physical materials or technology.

Real-World Projects and Investigations

Projects and investigations can teach students how science is connected to everyday life. For example, at the middle school level, projects can be constructed that involve the use of science in the following areas:

- Food and fitness
- Population
- Videos
- Environmental problems
- Farmland
- Careers
- Cars, boats, airplanes, rockets
- Business
- Sports
- Recycling
- Travel
- Space
- Cities
- Foreign countries

Additionally, projects and investigations can show how science connects to other disciplines, such as mathematics, social studies, music, economics, computers, geography, and so on. All of these activities bring science to life for students by showing them the usefulness of scientific ideas and techniques in a wide range of practical activities.

When to Implement

Students can be involved in projects and investigations at any time during the school year. However, you may want to wait until the first three or four weeks of school have passed before discussing the use and role of projects in the course. This gives students time to feel comfortable with the course content before they pursue their first project.

The first few projects should be rather simple and straightforward. Many students probably will need your guidance to formulate their first plan for a project. As the year progresses, however, students should be able to work more independently.

How to Implement

Begin by talking to students about the idea of a project. Tell them that you will be using projects and investigations for both instructional and evaluation purposes.

Discuss the process goals of instruction—problem solving, communication, reasoning, and connections—and point out their central place in the study of science. Tell students that their projects should be problem-solving-oriented and relate to the content of the course.

At the beginning of the school year, the first projects students work on most likely will relate to the content of the first or second chapter of their textbook. In fact, you may be able to use the textbook as a source for project ideas.

More Specific Suggestions for Students

To help students get started on their projects, share with them some specific guidelines for using a student log for formulating, researching, and presenting projects.

First, it is important that students be able to write down a clear description of what the project is about. Review and critique this description to make sure the student has not taken on a project that is too difficult. The project needs to be doable and it needs to provide experiences that contribute to the student's scientific growth.

Second, students should state what procedures they intend to follow in the course of working on the project. Does a hypothesis need to be stated and tested? Do measurements have to be made or data collected? Will library research suffice? Do interviews have to be conducted? Is a computer necessary?

Third, students should keep a written record or project log of their work. They should write down the purpose of the project, the procedure followed, and any materials used. They also should record any questions that arose in working on the project, keep track of data, and make notes of their thoughts and ideas about the project. And, they should decide how to best communicate results using graphs, charts, tables, or illustrations.

Finally, students should record their results. This final report can be presented as an oral or as a written report.

These steps can help students become successful investigators. They also provide important documents for you to use in assessing the educational outcomes of the projects and in shaping future projects.

Desirable Outcomes of Projects and Investigations

The use of projects in the science classroom can have many positive learning outcomes for students. In addition to developing scientific skills, projects provide opportunities for students to grow intellectually and socially. The following outcomes are a result of working on projects:

- learning to define problems and conduct independent research
- working with others when doing a group project
- finding out that real-world problems often are complex and require extensive effort over a long period of time
- seeing science as a practical, problem-solving technique
- organizing, planning, and pursuing long-term objectives
- discovering how to correctly use scientific materials
- practicing writing reports of investigations

Scientific outcomes of projects are many and varied. No single list can encompass everything students could learn from doing projects, but a general list of outcomes certainly can be written. Projects can be of the utmost importance in developing scientific capabilities because they provide opportunities for students to:

- solve and formulate problems in science and make applications to everyday life
- use scientific language to communicate ideas
- use analytical skills
- apply reasoning skills
- demonstrate knowledge of concepts, skills, and scientific theories and laws
- make connections within the sciences and to other disciplines
- develop an understanding of the nature of science
- integrate scientific knowledge into a more meaningful set of concepts

Evaluating Project Work

You need to evaluate project work by looking for evidence of the growth of scientific reasoning. If students have organized their projects according to the guidelines of this booklet; that is, if they have followed the steps of (1) writing a description of the project, (2) identifying the procedures they intend to follow, (3) keeping a written record of their work, and (4) stating their results. Then, an evaluation of the project is not only possible, it's rather simple.

The description of the project will help you identify the key scientific growth areas. Of course, these should relate to problem solving, reasoning, communication, and making connections. The procedure to be followed should help you identify more specific aspects of each growth area for evaluation. The written record and statement of results will let you see the student's thinking as he or she has attempted to complete the project.

Each project must be evaluated on its own merit. A written project can be used to assess a student's writing skills. If the project is presented to the class, oral communication skills can be assessed. A proof or solution to a difficult or nonroutine problem provides evidence of problem-solving abilities and reasoning skills. The collection, organization, and analysis of data provide evidence of problem-solving and thinking skills. The use of different techniques to represent or model a situation (diagrams, equations, or graphs) shows an understanding of scientific connections.

Projects can be evaluated on either a holistic or analytical basis. Holistic scoring is based on a project as a whole. For example, you can read and evaluate a sample of projects to determine a range of performance. Three to five categories can be established, and as you evaluate the rest of the projects, they can be placed in the established categories. After final adjustments, grades can be assigned.

Analytical scoring breaks the project down into specific elements or components and establishes point values for each one. For example, using the suggestions in this booklet, the following components and point values could be used to evaluate projects.

Element	Point Value
• Problem description	10
• Research method	10
• Project steps/work record	20
• Data	20
• Conclusions	20
• Project report	20
• Project grade	100 points

This analytical process provides checkpoints for individuals and groups undertaking long-term projects. One advantage of analytical scoring is that it allows for redoing and rewriting project elements, allowing students to receive maximum points on each element when they demonstrate mastery of the concepts and skills involved.

Cooperative Group Projects

What students understand about science can be enhanced by having students work together in cooperative groups. Working within a cooperative group allows students to pool their contributions to the implementation and outcomes of the project. However, the contributions of each individual may be lost unless a record is kept as to who has done what. This is important when group project work is being evaluated.

An evaluation certainly should be made of the group's performance, but it is equally as important to assess what each individual has contributed to the group. This may be most easily done by having a written log of group activities. Roles such as investigator, materials manager, recorder, and maintenance director can be rotated among group members. After the final group report is written, each student can participate in an oral presentation of the group's project.

For more detailed information on using cooperative learning in the classroom, see Glencoe's *Cooperative Learning in the Science Classroom.*

Sample Forms

A log sheet like the one on the right can be used for cooperative group projects.

Group Log Sheet

Group members ______________________________

Project ______________________________

Date	Work done	Questions	Results

A project record may require many pages to document information adequately.

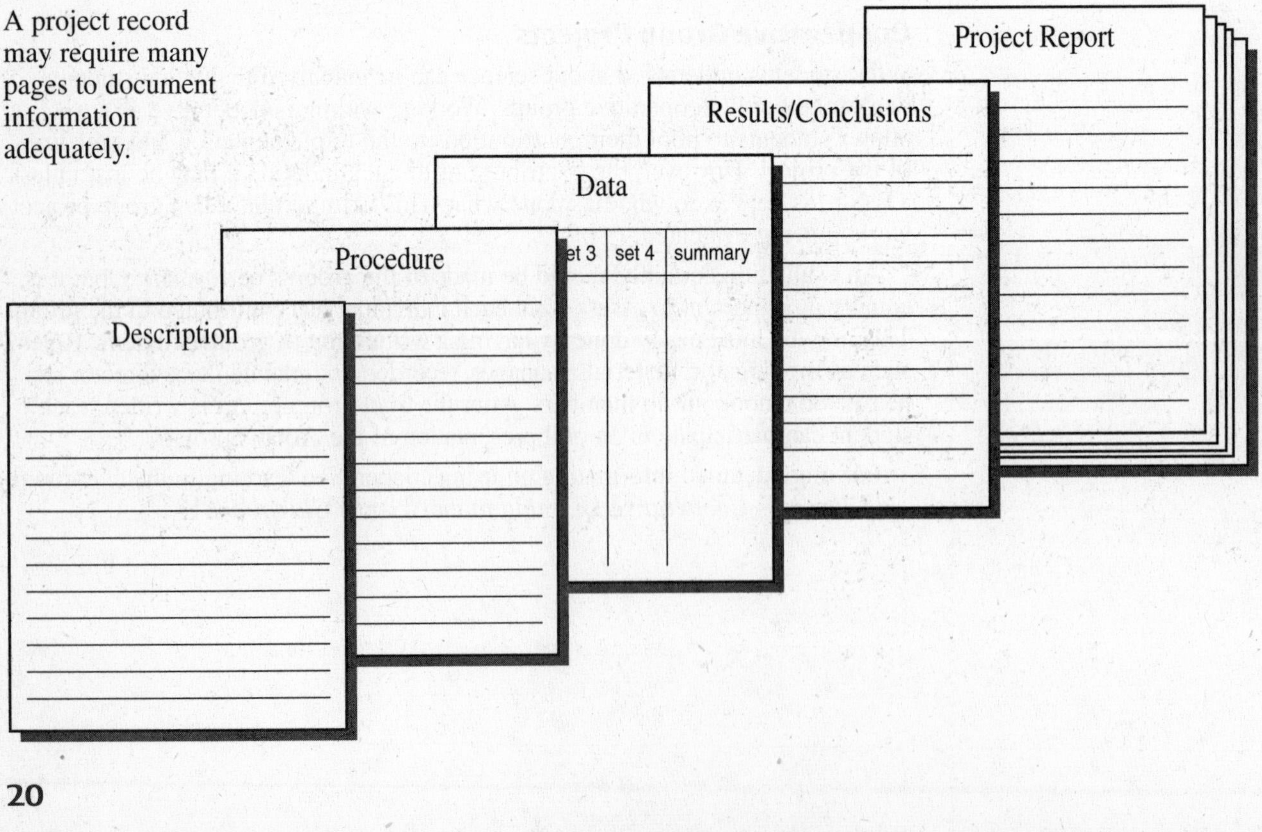

Portfolios and Journals

In This Section

Description

A portfolio is a representative sample of student work collected over a period of time. Portfolios tell a story about student activities in science. Their focus is on problem solving, thinking and understanding, written communication, science connections, and student views of themselves as learners of science.

A portfolio is not just a folder of student work. The pieces of work placed in a portfolio have more significance than other work a student has done. They are chosen as illustrations of a student's best work at a particular point in time. Thus, each item in a portfolio should be dated. The range of items selected shows a student's intellectual growth in science over time.

Portfolios can be used to assess performance on a range of science tasks during the school year. Have students collect their work for two or three weeks in a work portfolio. A review of the work portfolio provides a basis for selecting items that will go into an assessment portfolio. Assist students with the review but do not direct the process. The actual selection of the items by the students tells you which pieces of work the students think are significant.

Students should make an index that describes what they have selected and why. Student-selected items help you understand the students' views of themselves as developing "scientists." The student should submit a written reflection on the portfolio, documenting his or her growth in science during the assessment period.

A journal is intended to help students organize their thinking. It is not a lecture or a laboratory notebook, instead, it is a place for students to make their thinking explicit with drawings and writing. It is the place to explore what makes science fun—and what makes it challenging. The use of a journal is an excellent way for students to practice and improve their writing skills. Journal entries, of course, can be considered for inclusion in an assessment portfolio.

Examples of Portfolio Topics

The following examples illustrate topics that are appropriate for inclusion in a portfolio:

- a written report of an individual project or investigation
- examples of problems or investigations formulated by the student
- responses to open-ended questions or challenging homework problems
- excerpts from a journal
- scientific artwork
- a student's contribution to a group report
- a photo or sketch of physical models to illustrate a scientific idea
- teacher-completed checklists showing scientific growth
- the use of science apparatus, calculators, or computers in an investigation or problem-solving activity
- a scientific autobiography
- an applied use of science in another discipline

Balancing a Portfolio

The selection of work samples for a portfolio should be done with an eye toward presenting a balanced portrait of a student's achievements. As a portfolio is being assembled, keep in mind that selected samples should be representative of growth in each of the following areas:

- problem-solving skills
- reasoning and critical-thinking skills
- communication skills
- scientific connections

Other important curriculum considerations for portfolio samples are:

- statements on scientific attitudes, such as motivation, curiosity, and self-confidence
- group skills in working with others
- use of technological tools

Advantages of Using Portfolios

The use of assessment portfolios in science has grown out of the need to align assessment tasks with emerging curricular standards and also out of teacher frustration and dissatisfaction with paper-and-pencil testing. Advantages of using portfolios as assessment tools include:

- getting a more complete picture of student achievement and growth
- seeing complex and real-world tasks performed over a few weeks, rather than for speed and accuracy
- involving students in the process and encouraging self-assessment
- motivating students to study and learn science
- having an effective tool for parent-teacher communication
- encouraging the development of writing skills

Advantages of Using Journals

As students study science independently, the use of a journal can be very helpful in the development of a reflective and introspective point of view.

Types of journal entries include:

- labeled drawings and sketches with comments
- questions that occur to the student that he or she would like to be able to answer and the beginnings of answers to those questions
- detailed observations
- "what if...?" questions that are the beginning of planning an experiment
- sketches and notes about models and inventions
- thoughts about what is interesting and enjoyable about science class
- thoughts about what is difficult in learning science and how to overcome the barriers
- notes about interesting science items from newspapers, magazines, or television

Starting a Portfolio

Portfolios should be used throughout the school year. Begin by discussing the idea of a portfolio. Use the procedures outlined below to help you and your class get started.

- Have students use file folders to collect their work in a work portfolio.
- Ask students what they think should be included in an assessment portfolio.

- Discuss the format of a good portfolio—it should be neat, include a table of contents, and have a personal statement as to why each piece of work was included.
- Provide variety in assignments so the portfolios can reflect this variety—group work, projects, investigations, journals, and so on.
- Have students create their first assessment portfolio from their work portfolios.
- Have students review others' portfolios so they can see their classmates' work.
- Discuss how the assessment portfolios should be evaluated.

Discuss each student's portfolio with the student in preparation for development of the revised portfolio.

The initial implementation of portfolios will be a learning experience for you as well as for your students. As you both gain experience in using portfolios, their effectiveness in guiding instruction and for assessment purposes will be greatly increased. Although the use of assessment portfolios may seem like extra work at first, their continued use will enrich both the teaching and the learning processes.

Assessing Portfolios

In portfolio assessment, keep in mind that the pieces of work in the portfolio have been chosen by your students as representations of their best efforts. Thus, a portfolio is essentially a self-evaluation by the student who created it. Your goal in assessing the portfolio is to help the student gain additional insights into his or her scientific performance on the tasks exhibited in the portfolio. These insights involve growth in the understanding of science, strengths and weaknesses of approaches and procedures, and an analysis of both the kinds of decisions made and the final outcomes of the activities in the portfolio.

Ideally, you'll establish assessment criteria that can be shared with the students. The criteria of establishing and assessing a portfolio should be known by both you and your students. It is these criteria that form the basis for the assessment comments you make on the work in the portfolio. In creating a portfolio, the student then follows the criteria already established by you. Work is selected to represent the key goals of instruction.

Assessment criteria for portfolio evaluation are being established in school districts and science classrooms across the country. However, you may have to develop your own criteria. In so doing, you can develop those that are important to you and your students. The following section lists some ideas that can provide the basis for establishing your own assessment criteria.

Assessment Criteria

The assessment criteria for a portfolio can be organized into categories that align with the curriculum goals you're trying to implement. You can look for the overall quality of a piece of work in contrast to specific information or "right" steps being followed, or you can give a fixed grade for completing the portfolio process. Allow students the option of redoing certain elements of the portfolio in order to gain all possible points.

Assessment criteria should help you make judgments about student work. The criteria also should help you give fair and consistent evaluations to all students' portfolios.

Problem-Solving Criteria

Problem-solving criteria can be used to evaluate student performance in the following areas:

- understanding of problems
- use of various strategies to make a plan for solving problems
- ability to carry out a plan using models or technology
- analysis of results including statistical procedures
- formulation of problems
- creativity of approaches to complex problems

Language Criteria

These criteria apply to students' use of language to express themselves scientifically:

- use of correct terminology
- writing clearly to express ideas
- good organization of written work and journals
- explanation of results
- summary of key topics
- reflection on scientific ideas
- asking questions

Reasoning Criteria

Reasoning criteria aid the teacher in commenting on the following:

- identifying variables
- making hypotheses
- conducting an inquiry
- documenting results
- analyzing results
- critiquing ideas and procedures
- constructing, extending, and applying ideas

Other Criteria

These criteria involve the following:

- relating science to the real world
- making connections within science
- development of positive attitudes
- valuing science
- use of self-assessment and self-correction of work
- group work
- use of different scientific representations or models
- interpretation of ideas
- technology
- concepts and procedures

Sample Form

The sample form on the next page can be used to write assessment comments for a student's portfolio.

Assessment of Portfolio

Student ______________________________

Teacher ______________________________

Date ______________________________

1. Concepts, procedures, process skills explored ______________________________

____

2. Areas of growth in understanding ______________________________

____

____

3. Unfinished work or work needing revision ______________________________

____

____

4. Assessment of the following areas:

a. Problem-solving work ______________________________

____

____

b. Reasoning and critical thinking ______________________________

____

____

c. Use of language ______________________________

____

____

d. Other ______________________________

____

____

Other Types of Alternative Assessment

In This Section

Description

In addition to the major models of assessment discussed in the previous sections of this booklet, the following assessment techniques also can be used to monitor student performance:

- interviews and conferences
- student self-assessment
- student-constructed tests
- homework

These other types of alternate assessment methods are discussed in the following section.

Interviews and Conferences

Interviews and conferences provide an opportunity for you and your students to meet one-on-one to discuss science. This personal meeting can be a powerful motivating experience for many students. It also can provide you with a great deal of useful information about how your students think and feel about science.

An interview is a formal discussion that can be structured around questions that relate to a specific scientific topic. For example, a problem-solving interview would pose a problem for a student to solve. Working from a planned set of questions, you learn how the student goes about solving the problem. The student explains his or her choice of models and strategies to solve the problem, the procedure followed, and the meaning of the solution. Questions from you and verbal responses from the student are key ingredients of an interview.

A conference is not quite as focused as an interview. A conference is an informal discussion involving you and a student. Although a conference always should have a purpose—for example, to review and discuss a student's portfolio—it need not stay with that purpose exclusively. Let the student talk, ask questions, and discuss what is important to him or her. Appropriate comments and questions from you can elicit valuable assessment information that may be impossible to get any other way. (Sample interview and conference forms can be found on page 29.)

Helpful Hints for Interviews and Conferences

The following helpful hints have been suggested by the National Council of Teachers of Mathematics.

- Be ready ahead of time with questions.
- Put students at ease.
- Explain that you are looking for creative thinking.
- Pose a problem.
- Take notes.
- Be a good listener.
- Be nonjudgmental.
- Do any instructional intervention in a separate setting.

Student Self-Assessment

One of the real benefits of using performance assessment tasks is the opportunity to have students take part in the assessment process. When assessment is viewed as an integral part of the instructional process, its focus shifts from giving tests to helping students understand the goals of the learning experience and the criteria for success.

Implicit in all alternate methods of assessment is the idea that these methods can work most effectively when students know the goals of instruction and the criteria for measuring success against those goals. Knowing the goals and the criteria for success equips students to monitor their own progress.

Encouraging Self-Assessment

In order to help students learn how to monitor their own progress, explain the goals of instruction and the criteria for evaluating performances against the goals. The major instructional goals for the year can be displayed in the classroom and copies given to each student. How students will be judged on their work also needs to be discussed. Students need to know that right and wrong answers have importance, but that some new criteria for being successful in science are evidence of signs of growth in understanding and of the ability to think, communicate, and solve problems.

Encourage students to question their own work, strengths and weaknesses, accomplishments, work habits, goals, and attitudes. Periodically, ask students to tell you what they have done that shows progress toward achieving their goals. Ask them also to evaluate their own reports, journals, and portfolios and to provide evidence for their evaluations. All of these methods can help students learn how to assess their own work.

Using Self-Assessment Forms

One device that can be used for self-evaluation is a self-assessment form. You and your students can design such a form together. Then, every three or four weeks, students can complete the forms and give them to you. Typical questions include:

- What new understanding of science have you learned recently?
- Which topic is causing you difficulty at this time?
- Have you found any new topics that really interest you? Describe them.
- What do you enjoy and what do you not enjoy about working in groups?
- How do you feel about science now?
- What progress do you think you have made in science during the past few weeks?
- What can we do to improve our science class?

Goals of Self-Assessment

As students take a more active part in assessing their own work, they become more mature and responsible learners. Self-assessment helps students to work and think independently, set goals and priorities, and learn how to achieve success in school and in real-life.

The goals of self-assessment in learning science are more modest than those stated above, but no less important. Through self-assessment, students take part in the instructional process by evaluating their own performance. Their subsequent actions should result in learning more science, correcting errors or misconceptions, improving performances on more challenging tasks, and gaining deeper insights into the nature of science itself.

Varied Test Formats

For evaluation of basic skills and of factual knowledge, written tests are still an effective means of assessing performance.

Student-Constructed Tests

As an alternative to your regular tests, you might want to have students take tests constructed of student-made test items. Having students construct their own test items gives them a sense of participation in the assessment process. They enjoy making up the items and generally are very interested in the solutions.

A class can be divided into small groups of three or four students. Obviously, the test items need to represent the content being studied. Choose items from each group to include on the test. It is important that all students contribute to the test. If necessary, some items may have to be edited, but the essence should be retained. When discussing the correct responses, contributing groups can offer study suggestions for their test items.

Take-Home Tests

To add variety and interest to written tests, have students work on take-home tests. This is done by some college teachers, but is not usually implemented by teachers of middle and high school students. Take-home tests can challenge students with more open-ended questions or nonroutine problems. Time is not a factor as students can use all the time they need to complete the test. Take-home tests can be teacher- or student-constructed.

Practical Tests

Practical tests that cover topics in biology, geology, physics, chemistry, and other science fields offer yet another way to modify the test-taking regimen. These tools make use of physical materials and have students answer questions or perform various tasks. They can be teacher- or student-constructed and can be administered to individuals or small groups of two or three students.

Homework

Homework often is assigned and gone over in class the next day and then overlooked as a means of assessing student performance. However, this does not have to be the case. Some teachers have had success with assigning fewer homework papers but requiring that the assigned homework be included in the work or assessment portfolio. Certain carefully selected homework assignments could be reviewed and evaluated on a periodic basis. Skill types of problems or exercises occasionally could be included for evaluation; however the emphasis should be on thought-provoking questions. Thus, homework can play a more important role as an assessment technique.

Interview Scoring Form

Name: Date:	Score
Explanation of problem to be solved	
Explanation of strategies to solve problem	
Explanation of procedures followed	
Explanation of the solution	
Verbal responses to teacher questions	

Scoring:

1 = needs improvement 2 = improving 3 = good 4 = excellent

Conference Form

Name: Date:

Student questions: ______________________

Teacher questions and responses: ______________________

A Step-by-Step Model

This step-by-step model is designed to give you suggestions for using the performance assessment tasks in the next section of this book. It is based on a life science investigation, *Schoolyard Invasion,* found on page 33. The model incorporates sample forms, assessment tools, and the Performance Assessment Task Lists and Rubrics found on pages 89 to 178.

1. Before beginning, create some of the forms on page 20 in the Performance Assessment Toolbox section. The log and other documents will provide the means for students to gather and keep their project information in one place.
2. Choose one or more of the Performance Assessment Task Lists and accompanying Rubrics on pages 89 to 178 to give students at the beginning of the activity. This will allow students to see what's expected of them at the end of the process. You may use one or more of the task lists, revise it, or create your own, as necessary. The rubric on the back of each task list tells students what you'll be looking for when you evaluate their products.

In conducting this investigation, students may use the following processes. Listed next to each are some appropriate performance task lists and rubrics to evaluate the process:

Observing See Making Observations and Inferences pages 89-90.

Classifying See Making and Using a Classification System pages 121-122.

Collecting and organizing data See Carrying Out a Strategy and Collecting Data pages 97-98.

Making and using tables See Data Table pages 109-110.

Working within a group See Group Work pages 169-170 (also sample group evaluation rubric on page 32).

3. Assemble the following materials for the class:

   60 blue toothpicks
   60 green toothpicks
   60 tan (natural) toothpicks
   60 yellow toothpicks
   60 red toothpicks
   30 orange toothpicks
   stakes
   string
   food coloring

   Food coloring can be used to color natural toothpicks. Orange toothpicks will necessitate an additional category in the data table if honest reporting prevails.

   The school's baseball diamond or an area of field (approximately 30 m × 30 m) needs to be marked using stakes and string. The toothpicks are then scattered randomly over this area.

4. Divide the class into groups of three or four. Distribute the investigation section of the task to each group. After students read the investigation problem, tell each group that it will need to give you its procedures for review and approval before completing its investigation. After approval, the students will be allowed 30–45 seconds to complete the survey/hunt in the field.

5. After completing the collection process in their region, ask students to combine their results in a table like the one shown on page 32, or have each group make a table of its own for a final accounting of the "unknown organisms."
6. After analyzing the investigation results, lead a follow-up discussion. Questions could include:
   - Given the original numbers of toothpicks scattered, compare these numbers with the number of toothpicks observed and collected. Were there any difficulties in the observations and collection process?
   - Were you honest in your reporting? How were the orange toothpicks reported?
   - How did camouflage factor into this activity?
   - Did this activity relate to natural selection? (Color alone does not determine natural selection. Other factors include reproducing rapidly, adapting behaviorally, lack of predators, etc.)

Expected Outcomes There should be significant differences in the color of the toothpicks found in each area. Students may simply combine the orange numbers with those of the red or yellow toothpicks.

7. Select an additional form of assessment listed in the Performance Assessment Toolbox on pages 5 to 29 to evaluate one or more of the students.

Sample table for *Schoolyard Invasion:*

Region	Blue	Green	Tan	Yellow	Red	Orange
1						
2						
3						
4						
5						
6						
7						
8						
9						

Sample group evaluation rubric:

Group Evaluation	Group	Peer Group	Teacher
1. Clear and orderly written procedure for investigating region ____________.			
2. Data for region ____________ was recorded accurately.			
3. Tables were done in an accurate, neat, and understandable manner.			
4. Group worked together in an orderly and scientific manner.			
5. Information could be compared efficiently with other groups.			

Name Date Class

Life Science

Schoolyard Invasion

The Problem

It is February. The baseball diamond has not been used for several months. While we have been occupied with school studies and winter sports, something has been happening at the school's inactive baseball diamond. Just this morning, a registered letter arrived at the school with the following message.

Materials

- clipboards
- pencils
- collection bags

Dear Principal:

The following information is of utmost importance. A great scientific discovery has been made on your school grounds. Dr. I.C. Nuthings, one of the world's foremost authorities in the field of genetics, has been investigating sightings of previously unknown life forms. Her reports have revealed that unknown organisms have been sighted on your baseball field.

Although unconfirmed, these newly evolved organisms appear to be about 6.5 cm long and 1–2 mm in diameter. The initial reports also indicate that they come in a variety of pigments. Sightings have indicated blue, red, green, yellow, and tan life forms.

We are asking you, Mr. Principal, to assist us in our search for new knowledge. We need help with our preliminary investigation. Could you please gather a group of trusted students to help us? We need an immediate survey done of the area in question. I have enclosed a grid diagram of the baseball diamond, where we would like your students to begin their search.

Thank you for your cooperation in this manner. Remember, an orderly investigation of this matter could lead to great scientific discoveries.

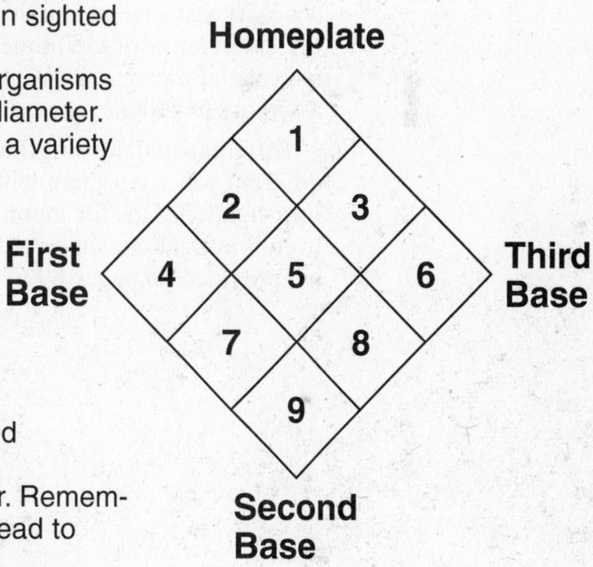

Sincerely yours,

Dr. C. Curitee

Our class has been chosen to conduct a scientific survey. Using the materials listed, we must make an accurate accounting of these unknown organisms that have infested the school's baseball diamond.

Investigation

1. Design a procedure for completing your task in an orderly manner. You are asked to investigate only one specific region of the baseball diamond. Your teacher will assign the area for which you are responsible. Label your collection bag with your name and region of responsibility.
2. In order to have an accurate recording of the expedition, Dr. Nuthings has suggested that we make data tables. As part of a larger investigating team, our class needs to decide on a single data table format. This is necessary in order to compare our information efficiently.

How to Use Performance Assessments

For each of the Performance Assessment tasks in this booklet, assessment strategies are included to help you determine whether your students have mastered the main concepts or skills of the particular activities. Some of these strategies include doing an activity a second time with a different hypothesis or changing variables. These assessments allow you to analyze the depth of student understanding and to give students needed practice in applying concepts and critical thinking.

These activities allow you to assess student mastery as they tackle a real-life problem. Students are given a problem and some ideas about what materials they might use to investigate the problem. They are expected to formulate a hypothesis, then plan and conduct an investigation. Students are responsible for devising a way to communicate the results of their investigation. They are also expected to draw conclusions about their hypothesis as well as the processes they use.

To take full advantage of these performance assessment opportunities, the accompanying Teacher Guide (pages 69 through 84) identifies processes and concepts that students might use in carrying each task to completion. Time needed in terms of total time students might spend planning and investigating is indicated. Preparation tips, materials, and alternative materials are given to make assembly of supplies inexpensive and easy. Expected outcomes are provided.

Different students or groups of students will approach the same problem in different ways, but there will be important similarities to watch for in each investigation. Tips for monitoring the investigations are included. For your overall evaluation, suggested Performance Task Assessment Lists and Rubrics are provided on pages 89 to 178.

Name Date Class

1 Physical Science

What materials are invisible to magnets?

The Problem

Magnetic levitation or "maglev" trains are the wave of the future. These trains speed along, suspended above the tracks, propelled by magnetism. At a town meeting in your community, people gather to discuss a maglev train project. Engineers insist that the system is safe, but many people disagree. After all, the train is "running on air."

Does the space between the tracks and the bottom of the train need to be kept clear for the train to run? What would happen if debris fell on the track? Which materials—perhaps a rock that's fallen onto the tracks—might interfere with the running of the maglev train? The designers of the system insist that much of the debris that would fall on the track is invisible to magnets, so it won't affect the way the train runs.

Materials

- bar magnet
- ring stand
- clamp
- 50 cm of thread
- paper clip
- tape

You are unsure about the problem, so you decide to conduct an experiment. Make a list of the kinds of debris that might fall onto a maglev track. Collect materials that might represent that debris. A pencil, for example, could represent twigs and sticks. Conduct an experiment to determine which materials are invisible to magnets.

Investigation

Caution: *Use care when handling sharp objects.*

1. Clamp a bar magnet to a ring stand. Tie a thread around one end of a paper clip, and stick the paper clip to one pole of the magnet.
2. Anchor the other end of the thread under a mass on the table. Slowly pull the thread upward until the paper clip is suspended below the magnet.
3. Without touching the paper clip, slip some paper between the magnet and the paper clip. Does the paper cause the clip to fall?
4. Try other materials and record your data in the Data and Observations Table.

Data and Observations

Materials tested	Result
paper	
cardboard	
glass	
plastic	
coin	

Going Further

Prepare a report about your findings. In it, include the following information:

1. Which materials were invisible to the magnet? Which materials were not?
2. Explain which materials could pose a hazard to the maglev train and suggest ways that people might protect the system from these dangers.

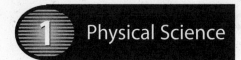

Name Date Class

2 Physical Science — The Challenge of the Moving Bottle

The Problem

It is the Monday morning after spring break and you are dragging yourself into science class. You soon learn that your teacher has not yet come back. Your substitute teacher shows the class a note that your teacher sent you. Can you meet the challenge?

Materials

- 1-L plastic bottle
- 100-mL graduated cylinder
- water
- petroleum jelly
- cork to fit bottle
- 10 straws
- paper towels
- 2 bubbling antacid tablets

PALM TREE INN

Dear Class,

I'm sorry I can't be with you today. I was not able to get a flight out of Hawaii, so I was forced to stay an extra day. Please work on this challenge today and show me your results when I get back tomorrow.

CHALLENGE:

You will be given a 1-liter bottle and the other materials listed on the board. You are to devise a way to make the bottle move on its own without you pushing or pulling it.

Good luck!
Ms. Higginbottom

Investigation

1. Begin your investigation by forming your hypothesis. Your hypothesis should state how you intend to make the bottle move on its own without a push or a pull from you.
2. Decide on a method of preparing and using the given materials. The illustration below could give you an idea, but you may design another method. After you choose your method, write each step out in a procedure that you or a classmate could follow.
3. Follow the steps of your procedure, and record your observations.
4. Were you able to meet the challenge? Was your hypothesis supported? Write a short lab report detailing what happened in Step 3.

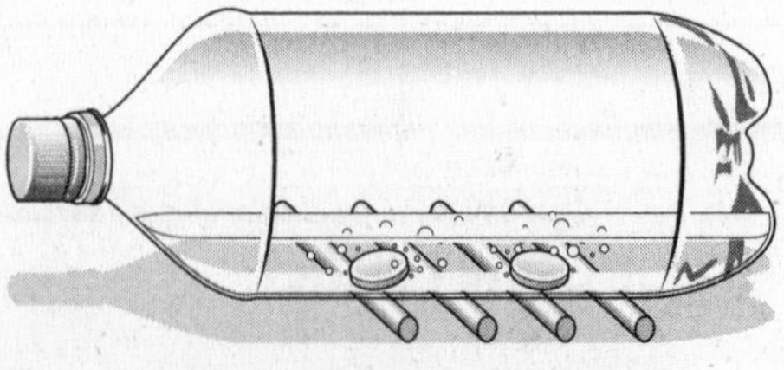

Going Further

Did your investigation illustrate Newton's third law? Explain how.

Name Date Class

3 Physical Science

The Moving Day Dilemma: To Ramp or Not to Ramp?

The Problem

Today is an important day for your family. You have just arrived at your new home with a moving van full of your family's possessions. Now it's time to get to work and start unloading.

As you open the rear door of the van and peer at the boxes inside, your dad says, "Well, we can use the ramp to slide the lightweight boxes down, but I'm afraid the heavy boxes will slide down too fast."

You have been studying forces and motion in school and you are sure that any boxes of the same size will slide down the ramp at the same rate of acceleration. After explaining your hypothesis to your dad, he tells you to go ahead and design an experiment to see if it's true. It will save you both a lot of work if it is! You search around to see what you can use to test your hypothesis. Above are the materials you put together for the experiment.

Materials

- 2 smooth, metal ramps or surfaces of equal length
- 2 small boxes of identical size and shape
- 2 stacks of books or boxes of equal height
- ruler
- weights
- clay

Investigation

1. Begin your experiment by stating your hypothesis based on the experiment you plan to do.

____

____

____

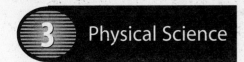

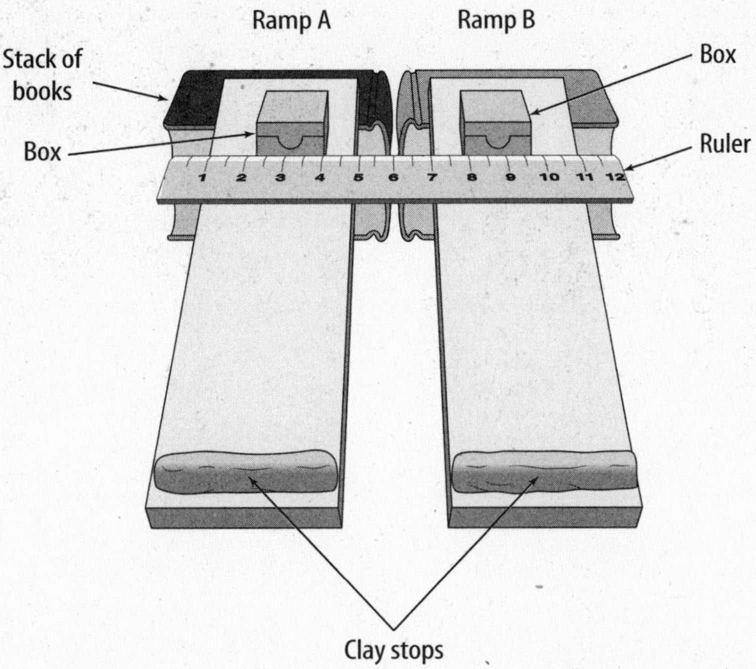

2. Decide on a method to test the rates at which two objects of different mass but the same size will slide down a ramp. After you choose your method, write each step out in a procedure that you or a classmate could follow.
3. Based on the steps of your procedure, construct a table to record your observations.
4. Follow your procedure with each object, running at least three trials to observe and compare the rate of motion of the two objects.
5. Analyze your data. Do your observations support your hypothesis? Write a short lab report detailing your findings.
6. What are you going to suggest to your dad about using the ramp to slide the boxes down?

Going Further

Does a heavy or a light object hit a stopper at the bottom of the ramp with more force? Design an experiment to find out.

Name Date Class

4 Physical Science

Identifying "Unseen" Changes

The Problem

You decide to have leftover soup for lunch. However, after dinner last night, your dad put the leftovers in the freezer. The microwave is broken so you can't defrost the soup in there. You decide to put the container of frozen soup in a bowl of warm water until it defrosts enough to safely heat on the stove.

When you place the container in the bowl of warm water, it floats. Because you are impatient, you try to speed up the defrosting process by pushing the container to the bottom of the bowl so that it is completely submerged.

When you do this, the warm water overflows. This surprises you. The size, or volume, of the container didn't increase and you didn't add more frozen soup, so you thought that the water underneath the floating container would simply shift until it took up the space above the container. But something changed. You decide to investigate why the water overflowed.

Using the materials above, conduct an experiment that will help you understand which property changed when you pushed the container to the bottom of the bowl.

Materials

- balance
- table tennis ball or small (3–4 cm in diameter) rubber ball
- water
- graduated measuring beaker (at least 900 mL)

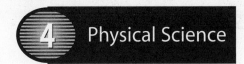

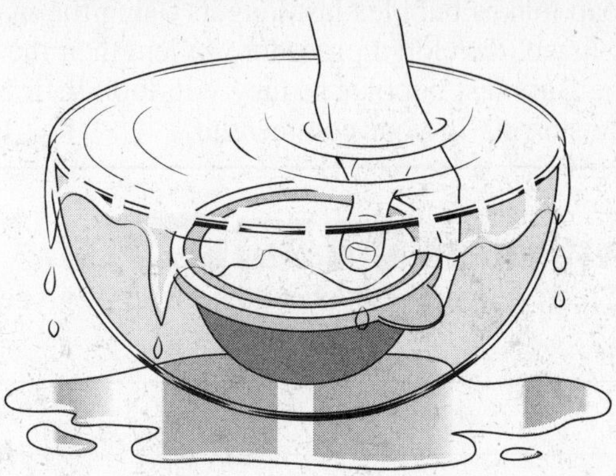

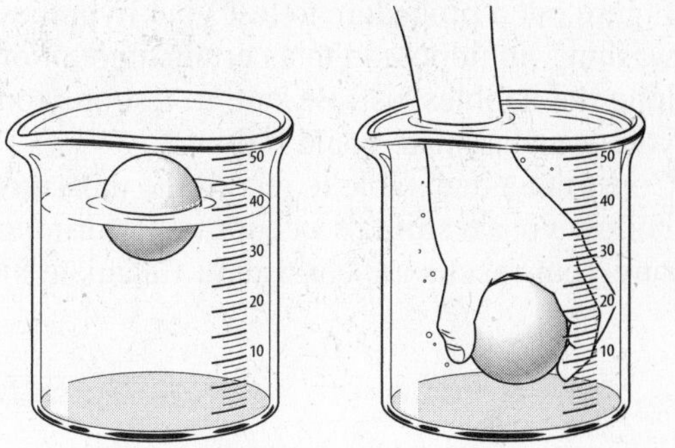

Investigation

1. Begin your investigation by stating your hypothesis about why the water might have overflowed. Keep in mind the physical properties of the objects and the relationships of those properties.
2. Decide on a procedure that will imitate what happened when you tried to defrost the soup. Write each step out in an order that you or a classmate could follow. There was no balance present when you tried to defrost the soup. Why do you think it is suggested that you use a balance in your experiment?
3. Follow your procedure, recording any information and performing any calculations that you think are important.
4. Do your observations support your hypothesis? Write a short lab report detailing your observations and data from Step 3.

Going Further

Try repeating your procedure with two objects in which the mass remains the same but the size of the container decreases.

Name Date Class

5 Physical Science

Making Bubbles That Last

The Problem

You work at an advertising agency and are in charge of directing a commercial for Bubblast dishwashing liquid. While filming the commercial, you run into a problem. The bubbles lose their "bubbly" quality before you are done filming. Since you are in charge, it is up to you to find a solution to this problem.

Luckily, you recall hearing that adding glycerin to soap makes bubbles last longer. Using the materials listed, develop a procedure to lengthen the life of the Bubblast bubbles so they will look their best while starring in your commercial.

Materials

- 4 jars
- 4 jar labels
- 100-mL graduated cylinder
- measuring spoons
- liquid dishwashing detergent
- warm water
- glycerin
- bubble wand
- spoon
- watch with second hand

Investigation

1. Create a hypothesis about the effect of glycerin on the duration of bubbles.

____

____

2. Figure out a procedure to test your hypothesis. You will need to consider how much glycerin and dishwashing liquid to add to a certain amount of water, how to make bubbles, and a way to determine how long the bubbles last. Be sure to test only one variable at a time. Write out each step in a procedure that you or a classmate could follow.
3. Construct a data table to record the measurements that you will make.
4. Follow your testing procedure to perform your experiment. Repeat the procedure two more times to make sure your results are consistent. Calculate the average time that a bubble from each mixture lasts.

5. Analyze your data and draw a conclusion that tells whether or not your hypothesis was supported.
6. Write a lab report that compares the performance of the bubble mixtures you tested. State which mixture you would use in your commercial.

Going Further

Try to find out what commercial bubble-blowing mixtures are made of. Are there any characteristics other than long-lasting bubbles that would influence your purchase of a bubble-blowing mixture?

Name Date Class

6 Physical Science

Thirst Quencher

The Problem

"Water water everywhere, but not a drop to drink" is a line from the poem, *The Rime of the Ancient Mariner.* Imagine a poor seaman on a ship far out to sea with no drinking water. At sea, there is water as far as he can see in all directions, but it's all salt water. Drinking it would make him sick.

Your task is to invent a machine that uses thermal energy from the Sun or from a lightbulb to turn salt water into pure drinking water. Use what you know to explain how your invention works.

Materials

- plastic wrap
- bowl
- saucer
- tape
- salt water
- heat lamp
- other materials with your teacher's approval

Investigation

Caution: *Do not taste, eat, or drink any materials used in the lab.*

1. Make a sketch of your invention and write a list of all the materials you plan to use. Have your plan and materials approved by your teacher. Your machine probably won't look anything like the fictional one below.
3. Make your invention. Use the salt water your teacher provides to test it. Find out whether the water is pure without tasting it.
4. Based on your test results, improve your invention.
5. When your invention is finished, make a poster showing exactly how it works. Your poster must demonstrate that you understand what is happening.
6. Turn in your invention and poster.

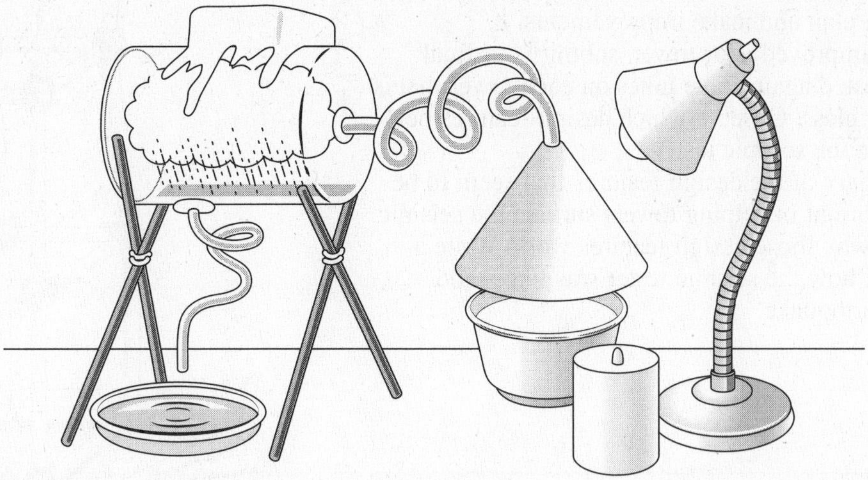

Going Further

Make your invention so portable and reliable that campers and sailors would buy it as an emergency water source. Find out how to apply for a patent for your invention.

Name Date Class

7 Physical Science

Making Straws Safe from the Shake

The Problem

It must be pretty scary to be in a house when an earthquake hits. First the light fixture on the ceiling starts to move, then drinking glasses on the shelf rattle and clink. Should you get into a doorway for protection, run outside, or hope it's going to be another "little one"?

Engineers have invented ways to make structures safer during earthquakes. Your task is to invent a seismic-safe tower. The tower must be at least 60-cm high and use only the materials your teacher gives you. You may design and use other materials to make a base for the tower to sit on.

Materials

- 24 plastic drinking straws
- 50 cm of masking tape
- pan balance
- scissors
- 40-cm × 40-cm cardboard

The total mass of your tower and base can be no more than 3 kg. Work with your classmates and teacher to plan how to simulate earthquake waves to test your tower. The tests must be exactly the same for all towers.

Investigation

1. Draw a design for your tower and be sure to include measurements.
2. Draw a design for the base of your tower, including measurements. Make a list of the materials you need. Get your plan for the base approved by your teacher before you begin building.
3. Build your tower and its base. Use a pan balance to make sure the tower and base don't exceed the 3 kg weight limit.
4. Attach your tower and base to the cardboard. You may be allowed to test your tower and base on the seismic tester. After the test, plan and make improvements.
5. After you've improved your tower, submit your final tower to be tested again. Take notes on each tower that is tested in your class. Observe which design features help towers survive the seismic test.
6. Write a summary of the design features that seem to be the most important in helping towers survive the seismic test. Explain why those design features work. Write a description of how the seismic tester was like—and unlike—an earthquake.

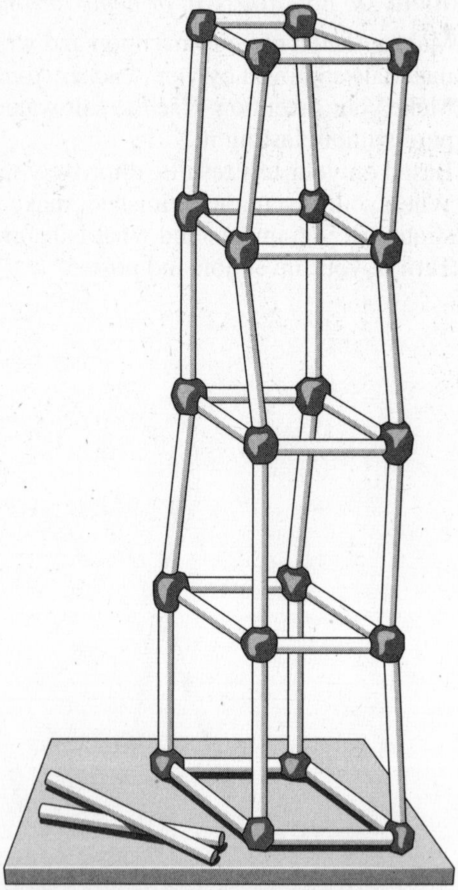

Going Further

Are the construction techniques that you found to protect towers from earthquake-like waves the same as the designs made by real engineers? Find out whether your ideas and theirs are similar. How do engineers test their models of seismic-safe structures? Work with your school's librarian to find addresses of engineering schools to which you could write to obtain more information.

Name Date Class

1 Earth Science

The Environmental Choice—Paper or Foam?

The Problem

You work in the Quality Control Department of Purebucks Coffee Company in Crystal Springs, Montana. Your company's policy is to always use the purest and most natural ingredients for your coffees. Also, your coffees are packaged in containers that can be recycled or disposed of in a way that does not hurt the environment. Management has asked you to find out which types of cups cause less pollution when they are burned: paper cups or foam cups. The company will present the results of your investigation in a pamphlet that they will give to customers.

Materials

- 500-mL heat proof beaker
- small metal jar lid
- 2 sheets of plain white paper
- matches (get from teacher)
- 3-cm × 3-cm piece of a paper cup
- 3-cm × 3-cm piece of a foam cup

For equipment cleaning:

- bucket of water
- dishwashing soap
- paper towels

Investigation

Safety Precaution: *Secure long hair or bulky clothing.*

1. Begin your investigation by stating your hypothesis. Which type of cup do you think will prove to be the least polluting? Consider whether you will be investigating air pollution, land pollution, or both.

____

____

2. Figure out a method to test your hypothesis. The illustration below shows one safe method. **Warning:** *This experiment must be performed outside on a calm day due to the fumes that are released by the materials as they are burned.* After you choose your method, write down each step of the procedure so you or a classmate could follow it.
3. Follow your procedure to observe what happens to the paper cup and the foam cup when they burn. Record your observations. You may wish to save the paper from under the beaker if it shows any signs of pollution from the burning.
4. Do your observations support your hypothesis? Prepare the results of your investigation in the form of a pamphlet detailing your findings for your company to distribute to customers.

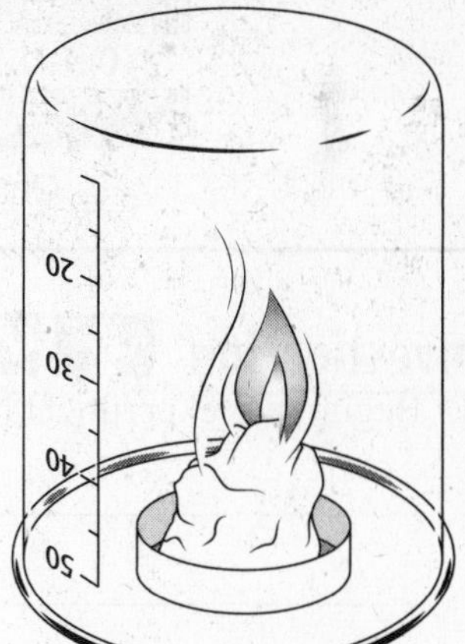

Going Further

In communities where trash is buried in a landfill instead of being burned, do you think it is better for the environment for paper cups or foam cups to be used?

Name Date Class

2 Earth Science

Limestone Weathering and Time

The Problem

You are a member of the city council in a medium-sized city in New England, where acid precipitation is a tremendous problem. Acid precipitation is rain, snow, or sleet that is polluted with sulfuric acid, nitric acid, or both. In recent years, the precipitation in some northeastern cities, such as Poughkeepsie, New York, has been as acidic as a cola drink.

The mayor wants to build a new city hall on the edge of a limestone cliff. You feel that this would be a big mistake because the acidity of the precipitation in the area would weather away the limestone and damage the building. When you tell this to the mayor, he responds by laughing and saying "Well, yeah, maybe in a million years!" He then tells you to bring proof of the problem to the next city council meeting.

Using the materials listed above, design an experiment to demonstrate to the mayor just how drastically acid can damage limestone in a relatively short period of time.

Materials

- limestone chips—chalk
- vinegar
- 3 jars with lids
- labels for the jars
- lab balance
- paper towels
- graph paper

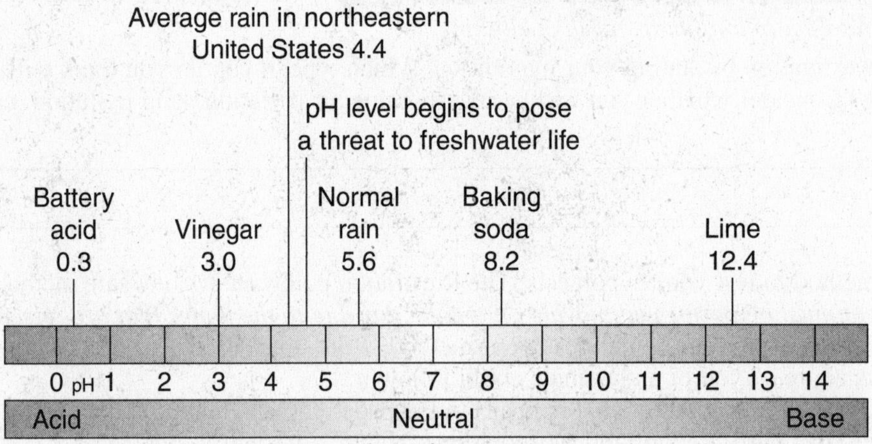

On the pH scale, acid rain is any rain with a pH lower than 5.6.

Investigation

1. Begin your experiment by stating your hypothesis, which will tell what you want to prove to the mayor.

____

____

____

2. Decide on a method for testing the weathering effects of acidic water on rocks. After you decide on your method, write each step out in a procedure that you or a classmate would be able to follow. Your procedure should include how to prepare the acidic water, how to test it, how long to test each group, and how to measure or record the amount of weathering.
3. From the steps of your procedure, construct a data table to list your measurements.

4. Finally, follow your procedure to test the weathering of rocks by acid for different lengths of time.
5. Devise a way to display your data from Step 2 on a graph. Then summarize in paragraph form what the graph displays.

6. Does your data support your hypothesis? Do you think the mayor will change his mind?

Going Further

What type of weathering took place in your experiment? What do you think the bubbles were that you saw in the experiment?

Name Date Class

3 Earth Science

Sky-High Costs: Are They Worth It?

The Problem

Billions of dollars have been spent on space exploration, but there are serious human needs on Earth that remain unmet. If you controlled all the money in the world, would you continue to spend some on space exploration, or would you spend it all on human needs on Earth?

Your task is to decide whether the money spent on space exploration is worth it, or whether it should be spent for other purposes. Express your opinion in a letter to your senator or state representative in Washington, D.C. Your letter must define the problem and support your opinion.

Materials

No special materials are required for this study.

Investigation

1. Your teacher will assign you to a group to research and argue for one side of this controversial issue. One way to think of the two sides is:
   a. Space exploration is important and funding should be continued at present levels.
   b. The space exploration program should not be funded because money is better spent to help people here on Earth.
2. After you're assigned to a group, conduct research to find information supporting your group's position.
3. Make a graphic organizer to display what you have found out about your side of the issue.
4. Participate in a debate of the issue. You are responsible for convincing the students on the other side that your position is the correct one.

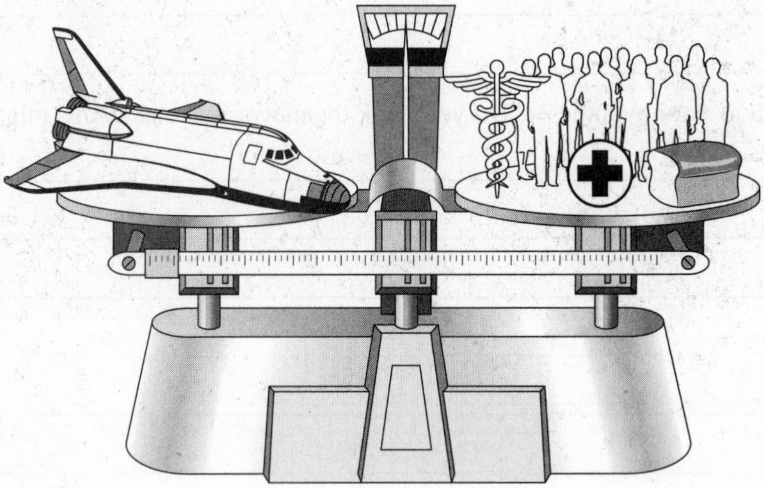

6. After you've finished the debate, decide which side of the issue you support. Express your personal opinion in a well-reasoned and organized letter to your congressional representative. Remember, your opinion doesn't have to match anyone else's opinion.

7. Go back to the group that was formed to debate the issue. Take turns reading your letters. Suggest improvement to one another's letters. Then, if you wish, revise your letter. Make the final draft as presentable as possible. Mail it to your senator or state representative in Washington, D.C.

Going Further

Plan and conduct a survey of your community to discover public opinion about this issue. Analyze the survey and write a letter to the editor of a local newspaper describing and analyzing what you've discovered. Remember to provide information to support your arguments. Mail your letter.

4 Earth Science

Your Fight Against Air Pollution

The Problem

This morning a registered letter arrived at your school from the mayor of your town. This is how it read:

Materials

- clean glass microscope slide
- paper cup
- clear tape
- plastic wrap
- rubber band
- meterstick
- microscope

Monday, March 30

Dear Principal:

I am writing this letter to ask for your help. Just last Friday I received a notice from the governor's office. It said that our town could get $100,000 in state aid for air pollution clean-up. To get this aid, we have to prove by the end of the week that we have enough air pollution to need the clean-up funds. One week is not very much time! That is why I am asking for your help.

Do you have a class of eager students who could serve on my air pollution task force? I need each student to choose a site where people may be affected by air pollution. Then, they must devise a test to count particles in the air at the sites they have chosen. Data collected will serve as proof that the source is polluting our air. For consistency, all air pollution samples must be taken at 1 m above ground level for a period of 24 hours.

Remember, time is of the utmost importance! Please notify my office when your test is complete.

Thank you in advance,

Mayor Wagner

Your principal has chosen your class to be on the mayor's task force. Use the above materials to come up with an air pollution test and to try out your test at a pollution source.

Investigation

Caution: *Use care when handling sharp objects.*

1. Begin your investigation by discussing with your group how to collect particles from the air in order to count them as a test for air pollution. As a class, agree on a method of collecting, observing, and comparing samples of air pollution. Remember that all samples are to be taken at 1 m above ground level for a period of 24 hours.
2. After the class decides on a method, each step should be written out in a procedure that everyone will be able to follow.
3. The class also should agree on a design for a data table in which to record information and observations.

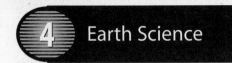

4. Next, state and record your hypothesis about the level of air pollution at a certain site. You may choose sites in your schoolyard or in students' yards at home.
5. Follow the procedure at your chosen test site.

6. Back in the classroom, follow the procedure your class decided on for observing and comparing your samples. Does your data support your hypothesis?
7. Decide on a way that your class should submit their findings to the mayor. Use a written or verbal presentation to show what you learned.

Going Further

Offer some suggestions for reducing air pollution in your community.

Name Date Class

5 Earth Science

Watch Out for Falling Rocks

The Problem

You are working at the local pet shop where you have been assigned to the aquarium displays. You just finished filling all of the new aquariums with water and are getting ready to go home when your boss comes over to you. He is pulling a wagon loaded with three huge bags of gravel. One bag has large, white pieces of gravel. Another has medium-sized pieces of blue gravel. The third bag has small pieces of red gravel. Your boss says, "Tomorrow morning I'd like you to mix up equal portions of each of these three sizes of gravel and put some of the mixture into each new aquarium. I think that it would look nice having all of the colors mixed together."

Materials

- 1 cup of large rocks (about the size of large marbles)
- 1 cup of medium rocks (about the size of regular marbles)
- 1 cup of small rocks (about the size of peas)
- tall, narrow glass or plastic container (at least 46-cm tall)
- water to fill container
- stopwatch

You have been studying the characteristics of sedimentary rocks in science class. You are not so sure that if you pour the gravel mixture through the water in an aquarium that the different colored rocks would still be mixed up when they settle on the bottom. You decide to do an experiment at home to see what would happen. Above are the materials you put together for the experiment.

Investigation

Caution: Use care when handling sharp objects.

1. Begin your experiment by stating your hypothesis.

____

____

2. You decide to do your experiment in two parts. In the first part, you want to test the three sizes of rocks individually to see how long each size rock takes to get to the bottom of the container. Develop a method for measuring and comparing the times. After you choose your method, write each step out in a procedure that you or a classmate would be able to follow.

3. From the steps of your procedure, construct a data table to list your measurements.
4. Follow your procedure to measure and compare the amount of time that rocks of each size take to settle to the bottom.
5. Analyze your data table. Does your data support your hypothesis so far?
6. For the second part of your experiment, you want to test all three sizes of rocks at the same time. Remove the first samples from the water and then develop a method for the second part of the experiment. Write out a procedure for this method.

____

____

____

____

____

7. Perform the test with all three sizes of rock together.
8. Does your data support your hypothesis this time? Write a short lab report detailing your findings. Include illustrations if you think they will be helpful.
9. What do you intend to tell your boss about his instructions tomorrow morning? Do you have any suggestions for a way to achieve the effect your boss had in mind?

Going Further

Of the rocks you tested, which size do you think would travel the farthest in a river? Why?

Name ______ Date ______ Class ______

6 Earth Science

Natural Curiosity

The Problem

Curiosity about nature leads to great discoveries. Scientists like Isaac Newton, Jane Goodall, and Albert Einstein started their work by asking questions. Like scientists, most young people ask lots of questions about the world around them. For example, you may have wondered how animals communicate, why falling objects fall downward, or why you felt like a car you were in was moving forward when the car next to yours backed out of its parking space.

Your task for this project is to consider the following question: Why does the water in a lake look clear and blue on calm days, but cloudy, and gray on stormy days? You will work with a group to come up with a hypothesis and to plan and build a working model to test your hypothesis. After you and your group have made observations using the model, you will work independently to write an evaluation of the hypothesis.

You may use some or all of the above materials to build your model.

Materials

- blue cellophane or clear blue plastic bags from newspapers
- blue food coloring
- flashlight
- gravel
- large rectangular pan
- sand
- soil
- sticks for stirring
- straws
- water
- any other simple materials that you collect

Investigation

1. Brainstorm with your group to come up with a hypothesis about the question: Why does the water in a lake look clear and blue on calm days, but cloudy and gray on stormy days?

____

____

____

2. Work with your group to plan a working model to test your hypothesis.
3. Use some or all of the materials provided by your teacher to build your model. If you would like to, you and your group can bring simple materials from home to add to your model.
4. Use your model to test your hypothesis. Take notes about your observations.
5. Write your own evaluation of the hypothesis.
6. Write a summary of how you used ideas about erosional forces, surface water, or shorelines. Did your model show effects of gravity or wind? Present your summary to your teacher along with your evaluation.

Going Further

Make a topographical map that shows the features of your model. Set up a class exhibit to display your group's hypothesis and model. Join other group to discuss your ideas about the project question and any new questions that came up while you were building and testing your models.

Name Date Class

7 Earth Science

Home Energy Study

The Problem

How do you use energy in your home? In this activity, you will be recording and analyzing the use of electricity in your own home. The project will last two weeks. At the end, you should be able to make some important conclusions about your family's energy-use habits.

Materials

- your home's electric meter
- electric bill

Investigation

Part I—Meter Reading

1. Begin by finding your electric meter. Take a meter reading every day at the same time, or as close to the same time as possible, for seven consecutive days.
2. Construct a data table that you can use to record the date, time, meter reading, and the kWh used for each daily reading. Below your table, provide a space to calculate the average kWh used per day.
3. Make a colored bar graph of the electrical consumption per day.
4. Repeat the entire procedure for another week while your family is trying to conserve as much electricity as possible. Enlist the help of your entire family.
5. Calculate the average kWh used per day during each week.
6. In your science journal, answer the following questions.
   a. Which day had the highest kWh / day? Explain why.
   b. Which day had the lowest kWh / day? Explain why.
   c. Discuss the differences between week one and week two of your investigation.
   d. How did your family conserve electricity during week two?
   e. What are some possible sources of error in your data?

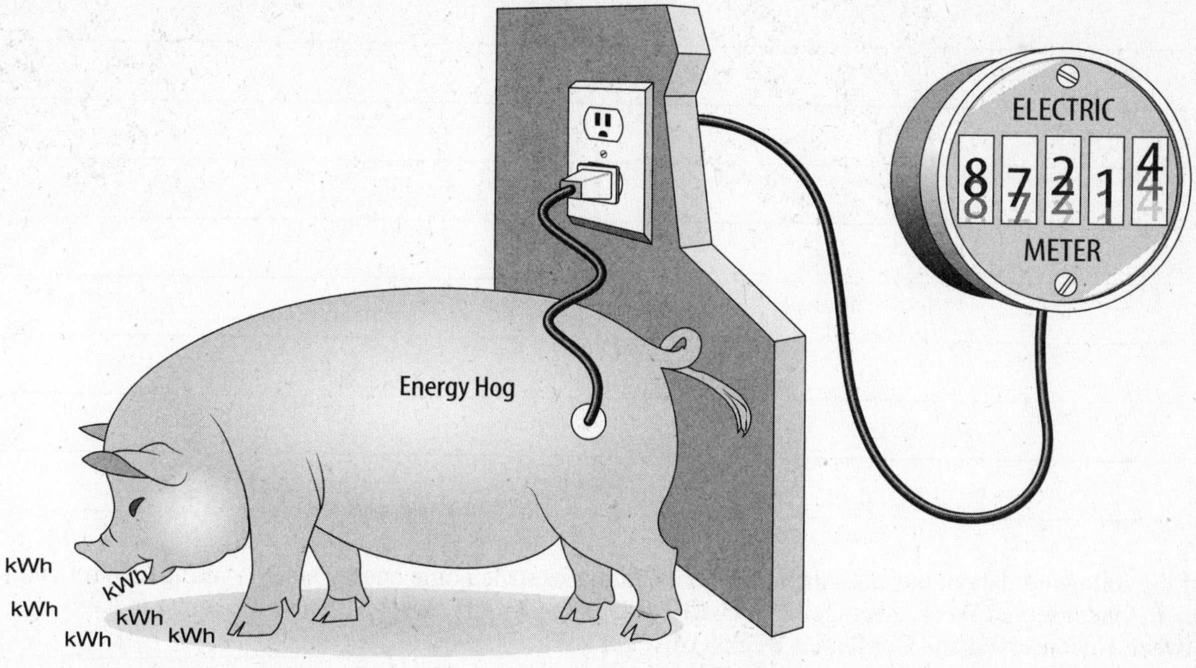

Part II—Electric Bill Analysis

Attach a copy of your home's electric bill to the report. Answer the following questions in your science journal.

a. What are your two meter readings?
b. How many kWh did your family use during in this period?
c. What is the length of this period?
d. What is the average kWh use per day?
e. What is the cost of one kWh?
f. What is the cost of fuel per kWh?
g. What is your average cost per day?

Part III—Personal Use

Make a data table giving an analysis of your personal daily electrical consumption. In the table, list every appliance you use, the wattage, the hours used each day, the kWh used per day, and the cost per day. Show a sample calculation for your table. Don't forget to include items such as the furnace, hot water heater, refrigerator, television, washing machine, and dryer. You may use the booklets in class to help you with the larger appliances. Answer the following questions in your Science journal.

a. Which appliances consume the most electrical energy? Why?
b. Which appliances consume the least electrical energy? Why?

Part IV—Conclusion

Write a conclusion discussing what you learned in this activity and how you can use this information. How can you conserve energy?

Put the following data in the class data table that summarizes the home energy study: Average kWh Used Per Day in Unconserved Week, Average kWh Used Per Day in Conserved Week, Percent Change in kWh between Unconserved and Conserved Weeks, Cost Per kWh.

Going Further

What implications does this study have for our country? Could conservation really make a difference?

Name Date Class

1 Life Science

A Collection of Marine Animals and Plants

The Problem

Until the 1970s, marine biologists thought that nothing lived at the deepest part of the ocean, called the abyss. It was too cold, too dark, and the pressure of the water was intense. Then new forms of life were discovered—organisms that no one had ever seen before. They don't require direct sunlight to live. Instead of photosynthesis, which uses the energy of the Sun, these organisms rely on chemosynthesis and use the energy from the breakdown of certain chemicals. With that discovery, biologists realized that marine life is found in all zones of the ocean, even the abyss.

Many of the familiar organisms of the sea, such as giant squid, dolphins, and jellyfish, live in distinctive zones in the ocean. These zones are defined according to how close they are to land and to how much sunlight they receive. This table defines the zones of the ocean. Read about the zones of the ocean, then collect at least five photos or drawings of animals and plants that live in each zone.

Materials

- magazines
- catalogs
- newspapers
- paper
- scissors
- posterboard
- felt-tip markers
- ruler

Ocean zone	Conditions
1. Tidal zone (part of the neritic zone)	the waters near shore, which are affected by tides and wave action
2. Neritic zone (part of the sunlit zone)	the shallow, sunlit waters above the continental shelf
3. Oceanic zone (part of the sunlit zone)	the sunlit waters of the open ocean, beyond the continental shelf
4. Disphotic or bathyl zone (twilight zone)	the middle layer of the ocean where sunlight is very limited; no plants live here
5. Benthic zone (midnight zone)	the bottom layer of the ocean (actually nearly 90 percent of ocean waters) where there is no sunlight at all
6. Ocean bottom or the abyss (midnight zone)	the deepest portions of the ocean floor, located near rifts, or breaks, in Earth's crust

Investigation

1. Begin the investigation by looking at the table of the ocean zones and then state your hypothesis.
2. Read about the organisms that live in the various zones of the ocean. Search magazines and books to find photos or drawings of these organisms.

3. Enlarge the drawing of the ocean zones and put it onto a posterboard. Draw pictures of at least five organisms you discovered that live in each of the zones. **Do not cut pictures from books.** Label each of the organisms and display your poster.

Cross-section of ocean

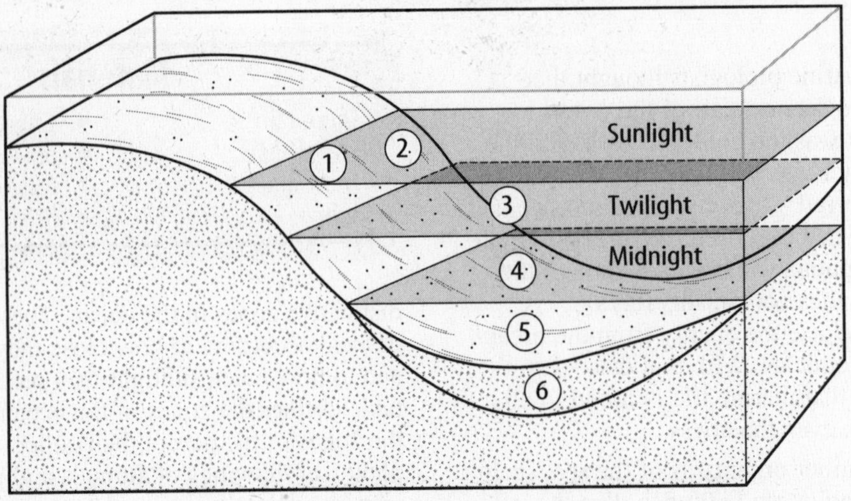

Going Further

Organisms that live in a particular ocean zone have special adaptations that help them survive there. Investigate the adaptations of some of these animals and add that information to your poster.

Most of the plants and animals of the ocean live in the sunlit zones of the ocean. Explore the issue of pollution in ocean waters and explain why, even though the oceans are very large, pollution is a serious problem.

Name Date Class

2 Life Science

As Alike as Two Peas in a Pod

The Problem

All of your lives, you and your twin have had people say, "You twins are as alike as two peas in a pod!" But just how alike are two peas in a pod? How about two acorns on an oak tree or two cactus plants? Identical twins look alike because they have the same set of genes, but most organisms within a species show variation because they have some genes that differ.

Differences between organisms within a species can be described in words or with pictures. Probably the best way to describe these differences is in terms of measurement.

Using the materials listed, determine a way to measure individuals of a species to show that there are some differences among them.

Materials

- a collection of plants or seeds from a natural source (not store-bought)
- metric ruler
- balance scale
- paper
- graph paper

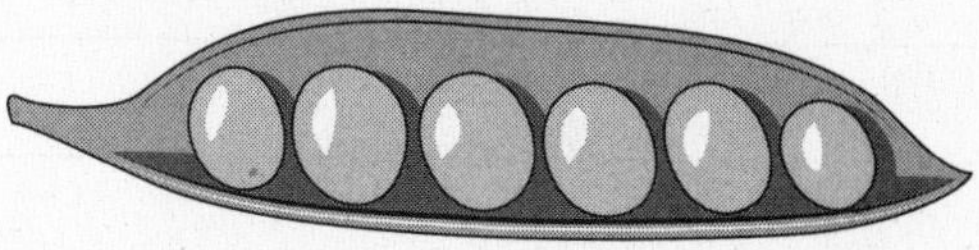

Investigation

1. Begin the investigation by stating your hypothesis. You might hypothesize that certain not-so-obvious differences exist among the plants or seeds that you have chosen to study.
2. Develop a method for measuring and comparing your subjects. After you choose your method, write each step out in a procedure that you or a classmate would be able to follow.
3. From the steps of your procedure, construct a data table to list your measurements.

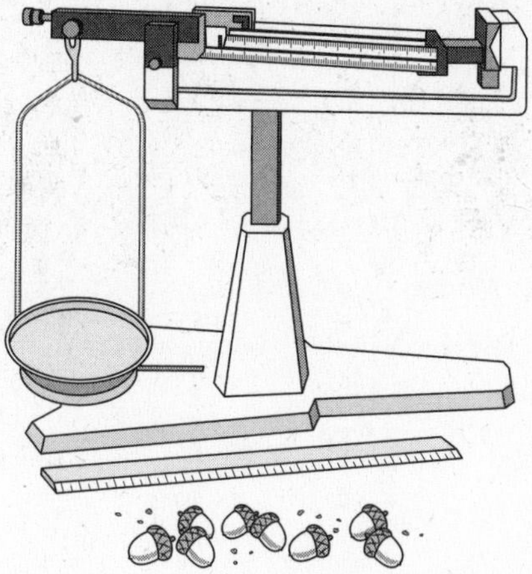

4. Follow your procedure to measure and compare the differences that you have chosen to study.
5. Pool your data with other groups who are studying the same trait so that you have data to analyze.
6. Devise a way to display the information from your data table in a graph.
7. Does your data support your hypothesis? Summarize in paragraph form what the graph displays.

____

____

____

____

____

____

____

____

Going Further

Choose a human trait that is inherited. Poll your classmates to find out about the variations of that trait among them.

Name Date Class

3 Life Science

Party Preparations

The Problem

One morning in August, you wake up to a beautiful, sunny day. Your visit with your cousin has been going great! Your aunt and uncle have just installed a swimming pool in their backyard and all of your cousin's friends want to help you enjoy this new purchase. In just two days, the two of you are planning a big pool party and everyone is invited.

You and your cousin quickly get dressed in your bathing suits and rush out to jump in the pool. You stop just in time. There's a green, slimy plantlike organism growing around the edges of the pool. Something has to be done. Nobody will want to swim in a pool looking like this!

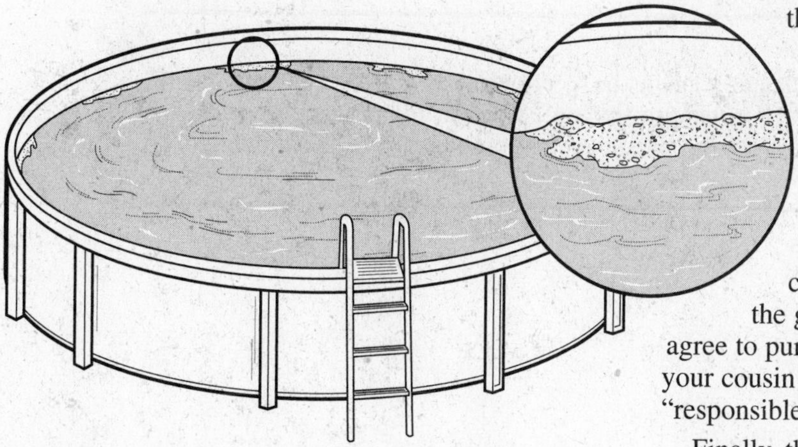

Upon consulting with your aunt, you find out that this "scum" is really an algae. You need to find out more about this algae and, even more importantly, you and your cousin need to find out how to get rid of it before the pool party.

Looking in the encyclopedia, you find the following:

Materials

- algal samples
- algicide
- test tubes (10)
- wax pencil
- droppers (6)
- test tube racks (2)

"Algae are plantlike protists that contain chlorophyll and produce their own food. If grown in the presence of sunlight, they reproduce very quickly. The light is used by the chlorophyll to make food. They have no root, stems, or leaves, and they live near or in water. Algae can kill other organisms in the water where they live when they are growing rapidly. They also give off an unpleasant odor and make the surrounding water unfit for use."

Oh no! Your aunt then tells you that it can be cleaned up using an algicide. An algicide is a chemical that stops the growth of algae. Your aunt and uncle agree to purchase some of this chemical if you and your cousin learn how to use the algicide in a "responsible manner."

Finally, those courses you took in science are going to pay off. Your uncle, who is a chemist, takes you to his laboratory where he supplies you with some materials and equipment. Using these materials, design an experiment in which you determine the correct amount of algicide to add to a test tube of algae. You want just enough to kill the algae, but you don't want to waste the algicide.

Investigation

1. Begin your investigation by writing a hypothesis.

2. Make a data table to record the results of your investigation.
3. Design an experiment to test the effects of the algicide on the algae samples. Remember to keep a control for reference.
4. While conducting your experiment, keep accurate records of your observations.
5. After completing your investigation, determine how much algicide is the correct amount to add to the test tube.

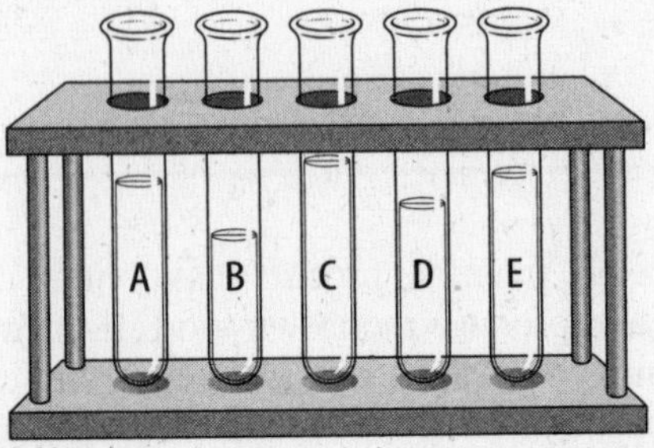

Going Further

Would common household cleaning agents be as effective as algicides in keeping your pool clean? Design an experiment to find out. What would be the drawbacks to using such chemicals as household bleach, soap, and mouthwash over commercial algicides?

Name Date Class

4 Life Science

Roots or Leaves?

The Problem

You've been planning your vegetable garden for months, and while you wait for spring to arrive, you grow some seedlings indoors. You water them every day, and you're amazed at how much water they soak up.

It's time to plant your seedlings outside, so you bring the tray of seedlings and your tools out to the garden. While you are working, your dog runs through your garden site, wrecking most of the plants on his way. On some plants, the roots are damaged, and on others, the leaves have been knocked off. "Oh, well," you sigh, after chasing your dog back into the house. "I might as well plant them anyway and see if they make it."

Materials

- 5 test tubes
- test-tube rack
- glass-marking pencil
- aluminum foil
- scalpel
- 5 bean seedlings

You know how important water is in keeping plants alive, and you remember how much water these seedlings needed. You hope they will be able to take up enough water to survive.

Using the materials listed above, design an experiment to find out whether a plant can take up water even if its roots or leaves are missing.

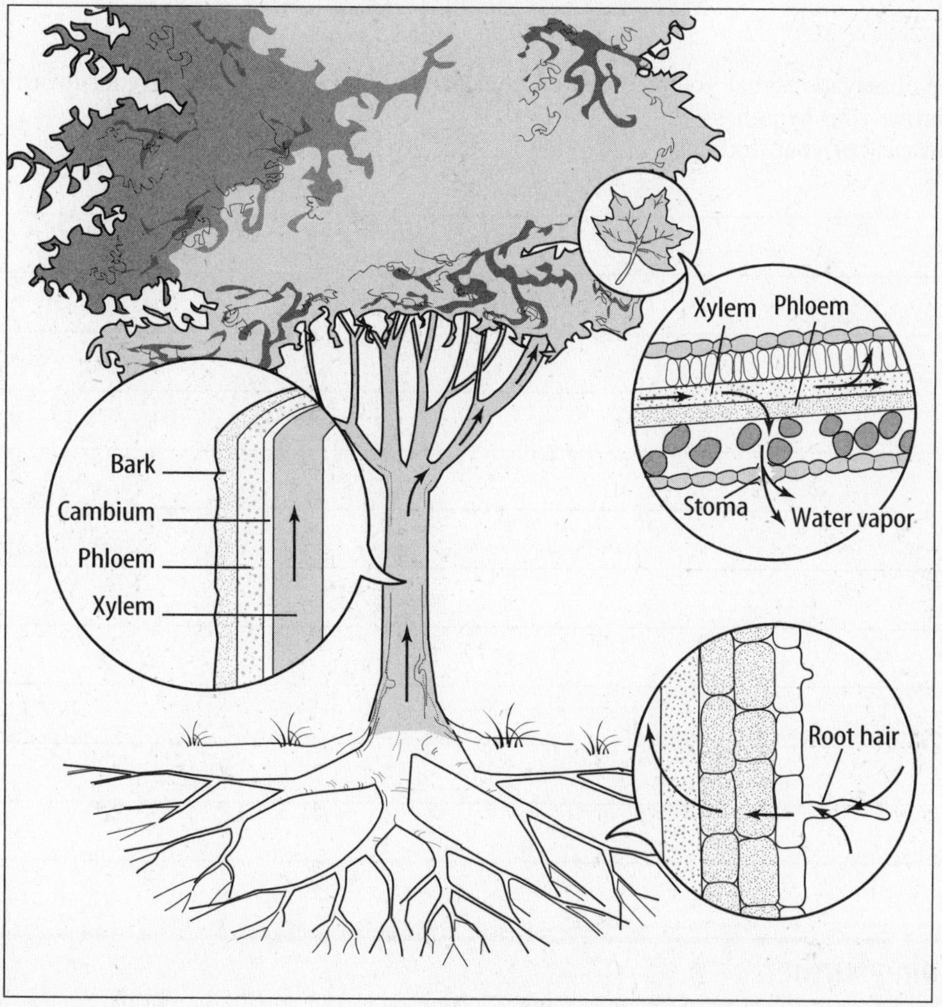

Investigation

1. Begin the investigation by stating your hypothesis. Tell what you think will happen in the experiment.
2. Choose a method of preparing, observing, and comparing the bean seedlings in each test tube. You may want to set them up as shown below. After you select your method, write each step out in a procedure that you or a classmate could follow.
3. From the steps of your procedure, construct a data table on which to list your observations and measurements at the start of the experiment and over a period of time.
4. Follow your procedure and record your observations and measurements.

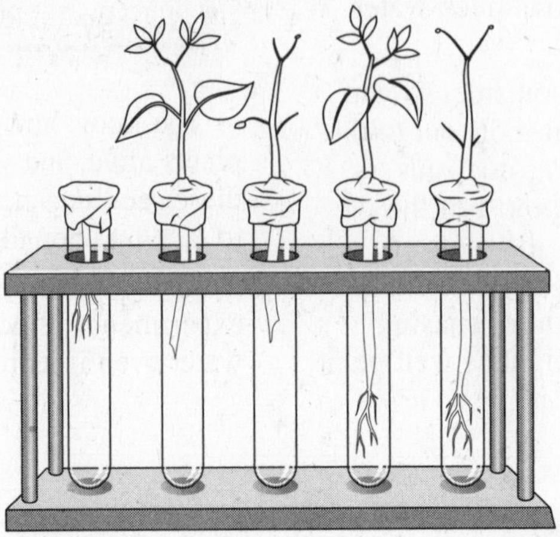

5. Analyze the observations that you recorded on your data table. Do the results of your investigation support or disprove your hypothesis?
6. Write a summary of your findings.

Going Further

What do you think would have happened if you had used seedlings that had twice the number of leaves as those you actually used in the experiment? Why?

Name Date Class

5 Life Science

Green Mail

The Problem

What environmental issues concern you? Destruction of rain forests, depletion of the ozone layer, acid precipitation, nuclear waste, growing population, and loss of topsoil are among the serious problems facing us. There are probably environmental concerns where you live. What environmental problem do you think poses the greatest risk to your local community or to Earth's global community?

Materials

No special materials are required for this study.

Your task is to select an environmental problem and voice your opinion about it through a letter to the editor of your local newspaper. You must define the problem and offer possible solutions to it.

Investigation

1. Brainstorm a list of environmental problems. Select the environmental issue you will write about.
2. Conduct your research.
3. Make a graphic organizer to help you plan what you'll say in your letter. Your job is to inform your readers and persuade them that your views are right. You must show your audience that you understand all sides of the issue. Remember that solutions to environmental problems often have serious non-environmental side effects.
4. Write a letter to the editor of a local newspaper discussing the issue.

5. Form a group with four or five other students. Take turns reading your letters. Suggest to each author possible revisions to his or her letter. Discuss all the letters and decide which should be mailed for possible publication. You can decide to mail as many of the letters as you like.

Going Further

Organize your classmates' letters into categories and publish them together as an educational booklet. Select a title, add illustrations and graphs, and distribute it to your school and community. Local businesses concerned about the environment may be willing to help you publish and distribute your booklet.

Name Date Class

6 Life Science

Choosy Pill Bugs

The Problem

Pill bugs aren't insects, they're crustaceans. Lobsters and crabs are examples of other crustaceans. As you work with pill bugs you'll soon see how they got their names—notice what happens when you touch them. Pill bugs breathe through gill-like structures and live in dry, sunny areas, in leaf litter and on the edges of forests. Decaying leaves, wood, and other vegetation make up their diet.

Materials

- 18 pill bugs
- plastic container
- paper towels
- plastic wrap
- tape
- test materials

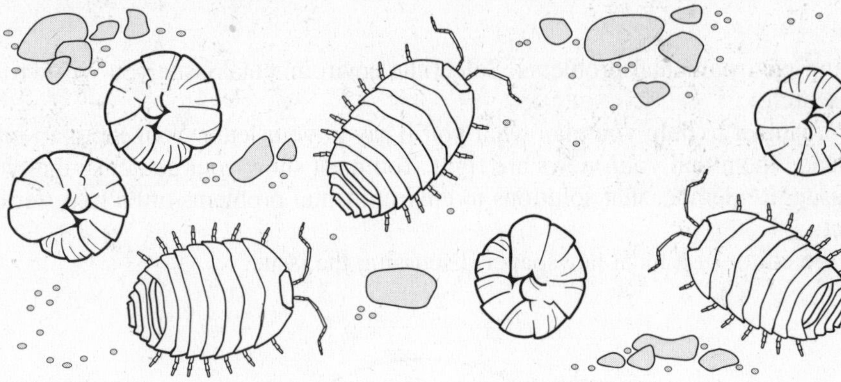

Use the materials listed to find out what types of things pill bugs prefer. You will present 18 pill bugs with a choice of two materials to go under or walk on. The purpose of this investigation is to find out what these crustaceans prefer; it is not intended to harm the pill bugs in any way.

When designing your experiment, be sure to restrict the choices you offer your pill bugs as much as possible. For example, if you want to know if pill bugs prefer bitter things more than sweet things, you wouldn't use a lemon and a sugar cube as your test materials. Why? With these two particular choices you would not be able to distinguish the pill bugs' preference for bitterness over their preference for dry things, or their preference for yellow things over white things. Also, plan how to prevent environmental conditions, such as light, heat, wind, and so on, from interfering with your results.

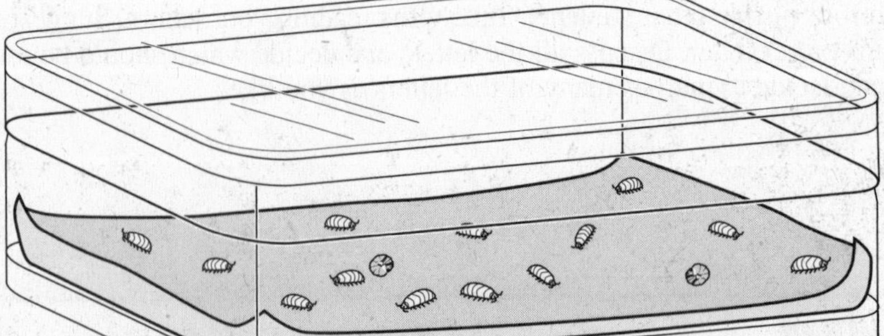

Investigation

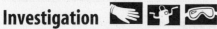

1. Prepare your pill bug container by placing a paper towel along the bottom. Tape down all the edges securely to prevent the pill bugs from crawling underneath. Make sure the sticky side of the tape isn't any place the pill bugs can get stuck on. The slippery, plastic sides of the container will prevent the pill bugs from escaping.
2. Keep the paper towel moist, not wet, during this activity so the pill bugs will be healthy.
3. Select two test materials for the pill bugs to choose between. Record these materials.
4. Write a hypothesis about which item(s) your pill bugs will choose. Write the reasons upon which you based your hypothesis.

5. Design an experiment to test which material is preferred by your pill bugs. Write down the steps. *Remember to cover your containers with plastic wrap to keep your pill bugs' home moist.*
6. Make a data table to record your observations. Make your first observations at the end of your class period.
7. Leave the pill bugs overnight and check on them again the next day. Once again, record your observations.

Going Further

You could repeat this activity using different test materials. If you had difficulty distinguishing which factors were being investigated in this experiment, you could try to narrow your focus with a second attempt.

7 Life Science

How sweet are you?

The Problem

When sitting in the school cafeteria, you often hear people making very different comments about the food they are eating (or refusing to eat). Although the food itself is the same, different people form different opinions about it, from "This is the *best* food I have ever tasted in my entire life," to "This is the *worst* stuff I've ever tasted, period!" Taste is definitely unique.

Taste receptors called taste buds are located in different areas on the surface of the tongue and on the roof of the mouth. Taste receptors are sensitive to stimuli that are bitter, salty, sour, or sweet. Different people prefer some of these stimuli over others.

At what point do people begin to taste something? What is the least amount of a substance needed in a food or drink for someone to detect the presence of that substance? Is this point or threshold different for every person?

Materials

- sugar solution
- water
- disposable cups
- 250-mL beaker
- disposable plastic stirrers

Threshold levels are factors that affect how food tastes to different people. Some people are more sensitive to a particular taste stimulus than others. The same soft drink can be perceived by one individual as being too sweet, while another person may perceive it as just right. In this investigation, you will design an experiment to discover your classmates' threshold levels to sweet stimuli.

Investigation

Caution: *If you are sensitive to sugar in any form, please inform your teacher.*

1. Using the materials listed, design an experiment to find out your classmates' threshold levels for sweetness. (That is the point at which a person can first detect the slightest amount of a substance.) Before proceeding with this investigation, have your teacher approve your procedures.
2. Use a data table to record your observations. Record a "+" if your subjects could detect a sweet taste and record a "−" if your subjects were unable to detect a sweet taste.
3. Test each member in your group, if permitted.
4. Upon completion of your group's investigation, collect all the data generated by your class. Make a bar graph of the class results. Compare the threshold levels and see if there are any patterns or trends.

Going Further

You may use similar testing procedures to determine how sensitive people are to salty and sour stimuli. What materials would you use for testing?

8 Life Science

The Care and Watering of an Exotic Plant

The Problem

Your grandparents were on vacation and brought you back a beautiful, exotic plant. The following care instructions were included:

Important! Once a week, water the plant with 100–200 mL of water that is approximately 5°C cooler than room temperature. Failure to follow these instructions will result in a nonflowering plant.

Because you are so fond of your new plant and its flowers, you decide to develop a method to prepare water that is the proper temperature for your plant.

Use the materials listed to develop a test to determine how to prepare the water. You need to find out how many mL of cold water must be added to 100 mL of room-temperature water to bring its temperature down 5°C.

Materials

- 2 water containers (foam cups)
- labels for water containers
- 100-mL graduated cylinder
- room-temperature water
- cold water
- stirring rod
- thermometer

Investigation

Caution: *Use caution when handling a thermometer.*

1. Write a hypothesis about how much cold water should be added to the room-temperature water to bring it to the proper temperature.

____

____

2. Decide on a method to add specific amounts of cold water to 100 mL of room-temperature water. Measure and compare the temperature of the water. After you decide on your method, write each step out in a procedure that you or a classmate could follow.
3. From the steps of your procedure, construct a data table to list measurements that you will make.
4. Follow your procedure at least three times to compare the temperature of mixtures composed of 100 mL of room-temperature water and varying amounts of cold water.
5. Using the results of Step 4, analyze your data and draw a conclusion about how much cold water must be added to 100 mL of room-temperature water to lower its temperature 5°C. If your prediction does not prove to be accurate, make another hypothesis and repeat the procedure. Repeat the procedure as often as necessary until you arrive at an accurate measurement.
6. Write a short lab report detailing your findings. Tell how you will use what you have learned when you care for your plant.

Going Further

What other instructions should have accompanied your plant besides those for water?

Teaching Strategies and Answers

Physical Science

Performance Assessment 1

What materials are invisible to magnets? p. 35

Processes and Concepts In conducting this investigation, students may use the following concepts and processes:

Observing
Comparing and contrasting
Recognizing cause and effect
Making tables
Interpreting data
Making inferences

NOTE: Use *Performance Task Assessment Lists* and *Rubrics* on **pages 89–178** to evaluate student work.

Time Needed This investigation should take two class periods to complete.

Preparation Each setup should be used by no more than four students. Assemble the following materials for each group in the class.

bar magnet
ring stand
clamp
50 cm of thread
tape
paper clip
collection boxes for gathered materials

Monitoring the Investigation Tell the students that you want to review their procedures for conducting their experiment and their list of materials to be tested. After student procedures and materials lists are approved, monitor their work and respond to questions and procedural requests.

Expected Outcomes This investigation examines magnetic and nonmagnetic materials. Students should learn that metallic items are magnetic and organic materials, including plastics, are not.

Going Further Students should realize that much of the debris that might accumulate on a maglev track will be nonmagnetic. Their suggestions may include using protective devices such as collars to enclose the track when it isn't in use.

Performance Assessment 2

The Challenge of the Moving Bottle p. 36

Processes and Concepts In conducting this investigation, students may use the following concepts and processes:

Observing
Inferring
Hypothesizing
Designing an experiment
Recognizing cause and effect
Communicating

NOTE: Use *Performance Task Assessment Lists* and *Rubrics* on **pages 89–178** to evaluate student work.

Time Needed This investigation should take approximately one class period.

Preparation For each group, assemble the materials listed on the student page. List the materials on the board, as specified in the note from the "science teacher." Each group will need approximately 100 mL of water and a dab of petroleum jelly.

Caution: *Aprons, safety goggles, and gloves should be worn. Students should be reminded not to point the corked end of their filled bottles toward people or breakable objects.*

Students may work in pairs to do the experiment, but the writing of the lab reports should be done individually.

Monitoring the Investigation Tell the students that you want to review their hypotheses and approve their procedures for building their inventions before they proceed. After students' procedures are approved, monitor their work and respond to questions and procedural requests. Students may use a variety of approaches to make the bottle move. They may use variations on the method illustrated on the student page, or they may come up with other ideas.

Expected Outcomes

Step 1

Each student's hypothesis should state how the student intends to make the bottle move.

Step 2

Students' procedures may include the addition of water to the bottle, the addition of the bubbling antacid tablets to the bottle, the corking of the bottle with the greased cork, and, finally, the placement of the bottle on the straws to allow for easier movement.

Step 3

Warn students that once the bubbling antacid tablets are added, they will need to work quickly and keep the cork pointed away from people and breakable objects.

Step 4

Answers to the questions will depend upon students' hypotheses and observations. Lab reports should reflect observations recorded.

Going Further Newton's third law states that forces always occur in equal but opposite pairs. Students may recognize that the cork moved in one direction while the bottle moved in the opposite direction.

Performance Assessment 3

The Moving Day Dilemma: To Ramp or Not to Ramp? p. 37

Processes and Concepts In conducting this investigation, students may use the following concepts and processes:

- Observing
- Inferring
- Hypothesizing
- Designing an experiment
- Making a model
- Collecting and organizing data
- Analyzing data
- Making and using tables
- Communicating

NOTE: Use *Performance Task Assessment Lists* and *Rubrics* on **pages 89–178** to evaluate student work.

Time Needed This investigation should take approximately one class period.

Preparation For each group, assemble the materials listed on the student page. Each group will need only a small amount of clay to make a stop at the bottom of each of their ramps. Wooden ramps could be used instead of metal ramps if they have the same smoothness. Each ramp should slope at the same angle. Two small boxes can be used to slide down the ramps, but one should weigh more than the other. Do not use balls or any other object that rolls. The boxes must have the same surface area in contact with the ramp. Two cassette tape boxes could be used, one empty and one containing a tape.

Students should work in pairs to do the experiment but should write their lab reports individually. The question in Step 5 could be handled as a class discussion.

Monitoring the Investigation Tell the students that you want to review their hypotheses and approve their procedures and tables before they continue. Be sure not to direct students to follow any set approach. After students' procedures and tables are approved, monitor their work and respond to questions. Make sure that the ramps are sloped enough that the boxes start sliding as soon as they are released. If the ramps are sloped at too low an angle, the boxes will have to overcome inertia to get started, and the heavier box will not start at the same time as the lighter box.

Expected Outcomes

Step 1

Students' hypotheses probably will state that an object's mass does or doesn't influence the rate at which it will go down a ramp.

Step 2

Students' procedures should describe the preparation of the two ramps and a method to release and time the objects. The illustration on the student page probably will be of assistance to them with this step.

Step 3

Students should repeat the test at least three times and record their observations in a table. Tables will probably look similar to the table shown below.

Which box reaches the bottom first?

Trial	Box A	Box B
1		
2		
3		

Step 4

Students' answers and lab reports should agree with their hypotheses and observations. They should have observed that both boxes got to the bottom of the ramp at the same time.

Step 5

Students' answers should agree with their observations. They probably will say that all boxes of the same size, regardless of mass, should be moved using the ramp. In your discussion, you might bring up the question posed in Going Further.

Going Further Students might suggest sliding objects of the same size but of greatly different masses down the ramp to see which makes a deeper impact in the clay at the bottom. They also could test to see how much a wad of paper at the bottom of the ramp is crumpled as a way to compare the force of each box. Note that the dad in the story had a good reason to be concerned. Although he was not correct that the problem had to do with acceleration, a heavy box sliding down the ramp might be hard to catch.

Performance Assessment 4

Identifying "Unseen" Changes p. 39

Processes and Concepts In conducting this investigation, students may use the following concepts and processes:

- Observing
- Inferring
- Hypothesizing
- Designing an experiment
- Collecting data
- Analyzing data
- Communicating

NOTE: Use *Performance Task Assessment Lists* and *Rubrics* on **pages 89–178** to evaluate student work.

Time Needed This investigation should take approximately one class period.

Preparation For each group, assemble the materials listed on the student page. Each group will need approximately 100 mL of water.

Caution: *Caution students to wipe up any spilled water.*

Students may work in pairs to do Steps 1, 2, and 3. The writing of lab reports should be done individually.

Monitoring the Investigation Tell students that you want to review their hypotheses and approve their procedures for carrying out the experiment before they proceed. If students haven't included the use of the balance in their procedures (to measure the mass of the ball), encourage them to figure out why a balance is included in the materials list for this experiment. Monitor their work and respond to questions.

Expected Outcomes

Step 1

Students' hypotheses probably will state something about the mass of the ball increasing when they push down on it, causing the water to overflow. Some students may realize that it is the density that has increased as a function of increasing mass.

Step 2

Students' procedures should describe a simulation of the original situation, measuring the change in water level, and an intent to explore the relationship of mass, volume, and density to explain what is happening. If they have not figured out why they need to use the balance, encourage them to measure the ball's mass even if they don't yet know what they'll do with the data.

Step 3

Caution students not to put too much water in their beakers. If the water overflows during the experiment, they will not be able to collect all the data they need to explain what is happening. Remind students to record their observations.

Step 4

Answers will depend on students' hypotheses and observations. Lab reports should reflect their observations. Since the balls used by the students each may have slightly different masses, individual calculations will vary. Students should understand that the formula $D = \frac{M}{V}$, where D is density, M is mass, and V is volume, must be used to explain the experiment.

Going Further Students might try putting equal masses of dried beans or rice in an empty yogurt container or in an empty 35-mm film container.

Performance Assessment 5

Making Bubbles That Last p. 40

Processes and Concepts In conducting this investigation, students may use the following concepts and processes:

- Observing
- Inferring
- Hypothesizing
- Designing an experiment
- Collecting and organizing data
- Analyzing data
- Measuring
- Making and using tables
- Communicating

NOTE: Use *Performance Task Assessment Lists* and *Rubrics* on **pages 89–178** to evaluate student work.

Time Needed Time will vary. Approximately one class period is needed to plan the investigation with an additional class period needed to perform it.

Preparation For each group, assemble the materials listed on the student page. Each group will need approximately 180 mL of liquid dishwashing detergent, approximately 135 mL of glycerin, and approximately 1440 mL of warm water. Measuring cups can be used in place of the graduated cylinders. Bubble wands can be made out of coat hangers by forming a 2.54-cm diameter circle with the hanger wire and leaving about 15.24 cm for the handle. Sugar or unflavored gelatin can be substituted for the glycerin.

Caution: *Students should be reminded to wear goggles and gloves, and to handle glassware carefully. Make sure that any parts of the floor that become slippery from the soap mixture are cleaned up immediately to prevent falls.*

Students may work in groups of two to four to do Steps 1–5, but individuals should write their own lab reports for Step 6.

Monitoring the Investigation Tell the students that you want to review and approve their procedures and data tables before they proceed. After students' procedures and data tables are approved, monitor their work and respond to questions and procedural requests. You should not direct students to follow any fixed approach.

Expected Outcomes Students' procedures should describe mixing a specific amount of liquid dishwashing detergent with warm water for each of the four samples to which varying amounts of glycerin were added. Students also may choose to vary the amount of dishwashing liquid, but the two variables (the amount of glycerin and the amount of dishwashing liquid) should be tested separately. Each setup should be tested three times. Measurements and calculations should be recorded in a data table.

Students should analyze the results detailed in their lab charts before writing their lab reports, stating which mixture they would choose to use in their commercial. Students' answers should agree with their data. Conclusions should state whether the students' hypotheses were supported or not.

Going Further Students will need to do some research to find out the composition of commercial bubble-blowing mixtures. A likely source of information is the manufacturers' labels from various bubble-blowing mixtures. Characteristics that students might mention that would influence their purchase of a commercial bubble-blowing mixture are cost, amount, and whether mixtures are nontoxic or nonstaining.

Performance Assessment 6

Thirst Quencher p. 41

Processes and Concepts In conducting this investigation, students may use the following concepts and processes:

- Inferring
- Recognizing cause and effect
- Inventing
- Making a model and poster
- Communicating

NOTE: Use *Performance Task Assessment Lists* and *Rubrics* on **pages 89–178** to evaluate student work.

Time Needed Allow students one-half of a class period to brainstorm and discuss their plans. Then allow students three days to finish plans and submit them for your approval. Give students a week to build their inventions and make posters. Provide another class period for students to demonstrate their inventions and display their posters.

Preparation Saucers should be small enough to fit in all bowls. Students must provide a materials list with their plan when they submit it for your approval. Students should supply their own additional materials. Plan to supply poster board and other art materials. You will need food coloring to test students' machines.

Monitoring the Investigation Check the equipment and supplies students plan to use. Assure safe practices.

Caution: *Students should be reminded to wear aprons, gloves, and goggles and to exercise caution when working with electricity. Supposedly clean water still may contain other chemicals or bacteria, so it should not be consumed. Warn students not to drink any of the water that they collect in their inventions. Make sure they identify safe ways to test the water.*

During one class period, have students demonstrate their inventions and display explanatory posters so you can assess students' understanding of what they did. Posters and machines also can be displayed at a school event, such as a parent meeting, at another school, or in a public place.

Expected Outcomes Students' inventions will vary. One simple machine using only the materials provided is a plastic-covered bowl with a saucer in the bottom. A small weight is placed over the center of the saucer. Water evaporates from the pool around the saucer, condenses on the plastic, and drips off the low point into the saucer.

Salt water with a drop of food coloring can be put into the "dirty water" reservoir and "clean" water that's collected can be tested for purity. One possible test would be to evaporate a drop or two of the "pure" water and look for crystals or other residue.

Going Further Some students may continue to refine their inventions and research the patent application process.

Performance Assessment 7

Making Straws Safe from the Shake

Processes and Concepts In conducting this investigation, students may use the following concepts and processes:

- Making a model
- Comparing and contrasting
- Communicating

NOTE: Use *Performance Task Assessment Lists* and *Rubrics* on **pages 89–178** to evaluate student work.

Time Needed Use one class period to plan how to make and use a seismic-wave simulator. Allow students one class period to plan their towers and two class periods to make them. Another class period will be required to test the towers, and a final class period will be needed for students to complete their writing.

Preparation Prepare a station with a pan balance and 3-kg mass, or a beam balance set to 3.0 kg. Provide plastic drinking straws, masking tape, scissors, and cardboard bases 40-cm square. Review other materials students plan to use for the base of their towers. Reject sharp, breakable, or expensive materials.

Monitoring the Investigation Students may work in pairs to build towers and bases, but writing must be done individually. Do not allow the straws to be attached with pins because of the danger of puncture wounds and blood. Ensure that students don't damage one another's towers. Work with the class to establish the rules for the tests of the towers. The tests should simulate earthquake waves and be identical for all towers. Pay special attention to controlling the size and frequency of the simulated earthquake waves.

Expected Outcomes Students' towers and bases will vary. Successful towers combine rigid and flexible materials to attain height and flexibility instead of breaking.

Going Further Students can compare the tower and base designs they found successful with the building designs recommended by real engineers. Students can research how engineers build models and test them for seismic safety.

Earth Science

Performance Assessment 1

The Environmental Choice—Paper or Foam? p. 43

Processes and Concepts In conducting this investigation, students may use the following concepts and processes:

- Observing
- Inferring
- Hypothesizing
- Designing an experiment
- Collecting and organizing data
- Analyzing data

NOTE: Use *Performance Task Assessment Lists* and *Rubrics* on **pages 89–178** to evaluate student work.

Time Needed This investigation should take approximately one class period.

Preparation

Warning: *This experiment must be performed outside due to the fumes that are released by the materials as they are burned. Students should wear goggles, aprons, and gloves. The experimental setup should be placed on a nonflammable surface, such as pavement. Bring a fire extinguisher outside with you. Remind students to be careful around open flames. Hand out matches one at a time. Secure long hair or bulky clothing. Be careful of the possibility of broken glass.*

For each group, assemble the materials listed on the student page to be brought outside. Buckets, dishwashing soap, and paper towels are to be used to clean the beaker and jar lid between tests and after the experiment is completed. The washing station can be shared between groups.

Students may work in small groups to perform the experiment, but pamphlets should be done individually when students return to the classroom.

Monitoring the Investigation Tell students that you want to review and approve their procedures for carrying out their experiments and data tables before they continue. Monitor their work and respond to questions and requests. Let students take their own approaches rather than using a single, fixed approach.

Expected Outcomes

Step 1

Students' hypotheses probably will state that the paper cup or the foam cup will prove to be the least polluting. Some might suggest that more smoke or fumes will be produced by one cup or the other. Other hypotheses might address how much solid matter is left after burning.

Step 2

Students may follow the illustration on the student page for setting up their experiments. Students' procedures should describe the placement of the material to be burned in the jar lid (which is sitting on the sheet of paper) and the covering the test material with the beaker after it has been lit.

Step 3

Remind students to record their observations. Observations may include smoky residue on the inside of the beaker, condensation, airborne particles, odors, and solid matter that remains after the burning.

Step 4

Answers will depend upon students' hypotheses and observations. Pamphlets prepared by students should reflect what they observed.

Going Further Most students will probably say that paper cups would be better to use in communities where trash is buried in landfills because they may decompose more quickly than foam cups.

Performance Assessment 2

Limestone Weathering and Time p. 44

Processes and Concepts In conducting this investigation, students may use the following concepts and processes:

- Observing
- Inferrring
- Hypothesizing
- Designing an experiment
- Collecting and organizing data
- Analyzing data
- Measuring
- Making and using tables
- Making and using graphs
- Communicating

NOTE: Use *Performance Task Assessment Lists* and *Rubrics* on **pages 89–178** to evaluate student work.

Time Needed Students will need one class period to plan their procedures and get their experiments set up. They will need some time over the next three days to evaluate the progress of their experiments and one additional portion of a class period to make graphs and write about them.

Preparation You may wish to have a class discussion concerning acid precipitation and the illustrated pH scale (after the students have read the first portion of their performance assessment). Make sure they understand what acid precipitation is and the problems it can cause, not only to buildings, but to plants, animals, and humans. Students also should be familiar with making graphs.

For each group, assemble the materials listed on the student page. Each group will need approximately one cup of vinegar.

Caution: *Aprons, gloves, and safety goggles should be worn as the students work with vinegar, since it is an acid. Remind students to wash their hands when they finish each day's work on the experiment. Students may work in pairs or small groups to do Steps 1–3, but Steps 4–6 should be done individually.*

Monitoring the Investigation Tell the students that you want to review and approve their procedures and data tables before they continue. Then, monitor their work and respond to questions. You should not direct students to follow any particular method.

Expected Outcomes

Step 1

Students' hypotheses should state that they are trying to prove to the mayor that acid can damage limestone in a relatively short period of time.

Step 2

Students' procedures will vary but may describe the preparation of three jars of water with a certain amount of vinegar, and the length of the testing period for each jar.

Step 3

Measurements and calculations should be recorded in a data table. Data tables will probably look similar to the following:

Sample	Time weathered	Mass of chips before weathering	Mass of chips after weathering	Change due to weathering

Step 5

Students' graphs will probably have Time on one axis and Amount of Weathering on the other axis. Paragraphs should agree with students' data in the data table and on the graph.

Step 6

Students' answers should agree with their data.

Step 6

Students should evaluate the effectiveness of their approach.

Going Further Students should recognize the type of weathering in the experiment as chemical weathering. They probably will need additional research to find out that the bubbles they witnessed in the experiment were carbon dioxide bubbles given off by the limestone. Limestone is made up mostly of calcite, a mineral form of calcium carbonate.

Performance Assessment 3

Sky-High Costs: Are They Worth It? p. 46

Processes and Concepts In conducting this investigation, students may use the following concepts and processes:

- Collecting and organizing data
- Analyzing data
- Communicating

NOTE: Use *Performance Task Assessment Lists* and *Rubrics* on **pages 89–178** to evaluate student work.

Time Needed Plan one class period for debate of the issue. Assign students to groups of four. Assign the same number of groups to each side of the controversy. Allow one class period for students to work with their groups to create a graphic organizer for their side of the issue. Plan another class period for the debate. Allow class time for students to write first drafts of their letters. The final draft can be assigned as homework. Plan a final class period for groups to share and discuss their letters.

Preparation Use the Performance Task Assessment lists for graphic organizers (students may select any one) and a letter.

Monitoring the Investigation Set time limits for each part of this project and hold students to them. Students must complete research and create an idea organizer before the debate. During the debate, make sure that students support their arguments with facts and attack only ideas, not the students expressing them. After the debate, neither side may have won. This issue is complex. There are many opportunities for compromise and many points that can be argued either way.

Students can return to their groups and take turns reading their letters. Group members should offer feedback about the strengths and weaknesses of letters. Students may revise their letters if they wish. Encourage them to mail their letters to their legislators.

Expected Outcomes Each student will have written a letter to his or her senator or state representative stating the problem and offering an informed opinion about possible solution(s).

Going Further Some students may want to know how adults in their community feel about this issue. Students can conduct a survey to discover adults' opinions and then write letters to the editor summarizing survey results, offering their own analyses and opinions. Point out that adults' opinions are not enough to decide the issue, especially if the adults aren't fully informed. Have students consider adding a question to their survey to find out how well informed their survey subjects are.

Performance Assessment 4

Your Fight Against Air Pollution p. 48

Processes and Concepts In conducting this investigation, students may use the following concepts and processes:

- Observing
- Inferring
- Hypothesizing
- Designing an experiment
- Collecting and organizing data
- Analyzing data
- Calculating
- Comparing
- Making and using tables
- Communicating

NOTE: Use *Performance Task Assessment Lists* and *Rubrics* on **pages 89–178** to evaluate student work.

Time Needed This investigation will need to be completed over several days. Take one period for the class to decide on a procedure and to design a data table. Students should then take their testing materials to their chosen test sites around the school or at home and leave them there for 24 hours. Allow another class period for students to observe their samples under the microscope and fill out their data tables. During that class period or the next, discuss the findings and have students prepare them in written or verbal form to submit to the mayor.

Preparation You may want to precede this performance assessment with a discussion of some of the possible sources of air pollution in your community.

For each student, assemble the materials listed on the student page. Make sure the students understand that the glass microscope slide must be clean for their test. Suggest that the paper cup, plastic wrap, and rubber band be used to protect the slide. Microscopes are only to be used in the laboratory.

Please note that the experiment portion of this activity should only be done in dry weather.

Set out materials in a convenient arrangement. Encourage the use of available supplies. Different and interesting approaches may require other materials. Additional materials may be needed to prepare a presentation for the mayor, depending on what is decided by the class. Possibilities include summarizing the results in a report, making a graph, or plotting the results on a map of the town.

Caution: *Make sure that students get your approval for their chosen air pollution sites before they do their tests. A variety of sites around the schoolyard are possible, or you might have each student take a slide home to test the air there, in order to get a broader sampling. Students may wish to label their test setups with "Do Not Disturb—Experiment in Progress" signs.*

Students can work together in groups to devise their procedure and data table and to compare data and present the findings, but should individually state their own hypotheses, test their own site, and analyze their own data.

Monitoring the Investigation Be available to the students as they develop their procedures and data table designs. It may be easier to divide the class into two groups, and each group can work on one of the tasks. As students work individually or in pairs to examine their slides, monitor their work and respond to questions and procedural requests. You should not direct student work in any single, fixed approach.

Expected Outcomes

Step 1

The procedure agreed upon by the class should state a logical method for collecting the air pollution samples, keeping in mind that all samples are to be taken at 1 m above ground level for a period of 24 hours. Most methods will probably involve letting particles from the air settle on a sticky surface. The method for observing and comparing the samples could involve observing the slides under the microscope, counting the particles in a small area, and multiplying to determine the number of particles per square centimeter.

Step 2

Students should prepare a step-by-step procedure list for everyone to follow.

Step 3

Data table design will probably be similar to this:

Name of person submitting sample	Number of particles			
	MSF 1	MSF 2	MSF 3	AVG

Step 4

Each student will have his or her own hypothesis stating whether or not a certain air pollution site is a problem.

Step 5–6

Encourage students to examine at least three different fields under the microscope so that they get a sampling of different areas of the slide. Students may find only minimal signs of pollution or no pollution at some test sites. Discuss whether a longer test period is necessary to achieve observable results, or whether the site can be rated "clean."

Step 7

A variety of responses would be appropriate here, including written, visual, or verbal presentations.

Going Further Students' answers will depend upon the air pollution sources in their community. Suggestions may include additional laws concerning output by factories, car-pooling policies, reducing fuel use in homes and commercial buildings, and so forth.

Performance Assessment 5

Watch Out for Falling Rocks p. 50

Processes and Concepts In conducting this investigation, students may use the following concepts and processes:

Observing
Inferring
Hypothesizing

- Designing an experiment
- Collecting and organizing data
- Analyzing data
- Making and using tables
- Communicating

NOTE: Use *Performance Task Assessment Lists* and *Rubrics* on **pages 89–178** to evaluate student work.

Time Needed This investigation should take approximately one class period.

Preparation For each group, assemble the materials listed on the student page. Students could be enlisted to help collect and sort the different sizes of rocks. Make sure that the containers are tall enough (at least 46 cm high) and that they are narrow.

Caution: *Students should wear aprons, goggles, and gloves and be reminded to take extra care if they are using a glass container.*

Students may work in pairs to do the experimenting, but lab reports should be done individually.

Monitoring the Investigation Tell the students that you want to review their hypotheses and approve their data tables and procedures before they continue. After everything is approved, monitor their work and respond to questions. You should not direct student work in any fixed way. Remind students that rocks should not be put down the sink drain.

Expected Outcomes

Step 1

Students' hypotheses should state what they intend to prove by doing the experiment. Some students may hypothesize that the rocks will settle in layers.

Step 2

Procedures should detail how they are to go about testing each size of rock, including where each rock is to be dropped from and how many trials are to be done for each type of specimen.

Step 3

Measurements and calculations should be recorded in a data table. Data tables may look similar to the following:

Rock size	1	2	3	4	Average
large					
medium					
small					

Step 5

Answers will depend upon students' hypotheses and observations.

Step 6

Procedures should describe how students intend to test all three of the different sized rocks at the same time, including how they are to be mixed together and deposited in the water. Procedures should include how observations are to be recorded.

Step 8

There will be varying answers depending upon students' hypotheses and observations. Most students probably will report that the rocks settled in layers.

Step 9

Answers will depend upon students' hypotheses and observations. A better method might be to mix the gravel and put the mixture in the aquarium before the water is added, and to add water slowly so as not to disturb the gravel mixture.

Going Further Students will probably state that the smallest rocks would travel farther in a river because they are lighter and the river would carry them along and not let them sink.

Performance Assessment 6

Natural Curiosity p. 52

Processes and Concepts In conducting this investigation, students may use the following concepts and processes:

- Hypothesizing
- Making a model
- Analyzing data

NOTE: Use *Performance Task Assessment Lists* and *Rubrics* on **pages 89–178** to evaluate student work.

Time Needed Allow students part of one class period to discuss a possible hypothesis to explain the observation that on clear days, the water of a lake looks clear and blue, but on stormy days, the water looks cloudy and gray.

Allow an entire class period for groups to choose a hypothesis and plan a working model that they can use to test the hypothesis. Have student teams build the model as homework or allow parts of several class periods for students to put the model together and test their hypothesis. As homework, each student can use the group's data to write an evaluation of his or her hypothesis.

Preparation Use the Performance Task Assessment lists for formulating a hypothesis, making a model, and evaluating a hypothesis.

Monitoring the Investigation Students will work in groups to decide on hypotheses and to build and use the models. Each student will write an evaluation of the hypothesis independently.

After students have written their evaluations, engage them in a brief discussion about their hypotheses. Challenge students to point out questions that still remain about the initial topic and have them suggest new models or experiments that could address their questions.

Expected Outcomes Most student hypotheses will center around the behavior of particles in a body of water. Some working models may show how wave action caused by wind mixes particles of sand and soil with the water, causing the appearance of the water to change. Some students may hypothesize that the reflection of a blue sky is the reason why water looks clear and blue on calm days and cloudy and gray on cloudy, stormy days.

After working with their models, students' evaluations should indicate that in clear water, soil particles settle to the bottom while in cloudy water, particles are mixed up in the water. The reflection of light has some part in the appearance of the water, but water without light will still appear clear, not cloudy.

Going Further Have students display the models and hypotheses. Some students might make topographic maps showing the features of their models. Encourage discussion about the hypotheses students came up with for the project and any new questions that arose during the course of the investigation.

Performance Assessment 7

Home Energy Study p. 53

Processes and Concepts In conducting this investigation, students may use the following concepts and processes:

Observing
Controlling variables
Calculating
Communicating
Evaluation
Measuring
Interpreting data
Analysis
Making charts
Making graphs

NOTE: Use *Performance Task Assessment Lists* and *Rubrics* on **pages 89–178** to evaluate student work.

Time Needed Students will need at least two weeks to complete this investigation, but most of it can be done as homework. Part of one class period will be needed to teach meter reading. It is very helpful to take a few minutes at the beginning of each class during the project to help students record their data and to troubleshoot problems they may encounter. One class period will be needed to help students read their electric bill and to teach students how to calculate kWh used by an appliance. One class period at the end of the study will be needed for students to calculate and record their data on the class data chart. A class period, or part of a class period, will be needed for discussion of class results and their implications.

Preparation Obtain free education materials from your local electric company. These usually include pamphlets with average kWh or wattage for common appliances, handouts on how to read an electric meter, sample electric bills, and information on how to interpret an electric bill.

Introduce the activity by displaying electric meters or pictures of electric meters. Old meters may be available from your local electric company. Do some practice readings. Check readings daily to help monitor student progress. Be sure students are not reading their water or gas meters.

Ask students to save an old electric bill several weeks before they need it. A photocopy is fine. If students cannot produce a bill, use one provided by the electric company. Help students analyze their bills in class. Teach students how to calculate kWh for various appliances. Good examples include an electric hair dryer, an electric curling iron, and a toaster. Do sample calculations together in class. Discuss where students may find the wattage of an appliance.

Monitoring the Investigation Help may be needed as students calculate the percent change in kWh per day between the conserved and unconserved weeks. Discuss the fact that percent change is more important than raw change in kWh because it allows comparison in spite of variation in house size and electric usage.

Short daily checks on this activity will be very helpful. You will be able to identify problems and motivate students to stay with the project. Construct large class data tables for students to record their final data. Discuss the class averages from the class data table. Discuss trends in appliances with high kWh, such as those that make or use heat or have a high resistance. Discuss ways students conserved electricity in their homes. Most students are enthusiastic about environmental issues.

Expected Outcomes Students, with the help of their families, probably will be able to significantly reduce their electrical consumption. This data will be affected by any major fluctuations in factors, such as changes in the daily weather that cause a considerable difference in heat or air conditioning.

Going Further Have students share their results in an article for the school or hometown newspaper. The local electric company would be another audience for results from this study.

Life Science

Performance Assessment 1

A Collection of Marine Animals and Plants p. 55

Processes and Concepts In conducting this investigation, students may use the following concepts and processes:

Researching
Comparing and contrasting
Recognizing cause and effect
Making tables and posters
Interpreting illustrations
Making inferences

NOTE: Use *Performance Task Assessment Lists* and *Rubrics* on **pages 89–178** to evaluate student work.

Time Needed Have students begin to search for photos and drawings of ocean animals and plants as soon as they begin the unit. Instruct them to make copies of the materials they find and include notes about where the animals live in the ocean. They may work on their posters outside of class if desired. One class period should be spent discussing the finished posters. If desired, integrate all of the organisms on a master poster and display it on a bulletin board.

Preparation Introduce the idea of layers of light, temperature, and pressure in the ocean and have students hypothesize about the effects that these conditions might have on plants and animals and how they adapt.

Monitoring the Investigation Remind students that you want to review their hypotheses about the effects that pressure in the ocean have on plants and animals and their adaptations. Encourage students to choose from different zones so that they can compare and contrast the plants and animals. After the hypotheses have been approved, monitor their work and respond to questions and procedural requests.

Expected Outcomes This investigation examines the life zones in the ocean and the factors that determine them. Students should learn that different oceanic conditions require specialized adaptations.

Going Further Students should learn about the adaptations and vast diversity of marine animals and plants like kelp, sharks, lantern fish, dolphins, sperm whales, and tube worms. As they learn that most of the life in the ocean is confined to the top ten percent of its waters, the dangers of ocean pollution become clearer.

Performance Assessment 2

As Alike As Two Peas in a Pod p. 57

Processes and Concepts In conducting this investigation, students may use the following concepts and processes:

Observing
Inferring
Hypothesizing
Collecting data
Analyzing data
Measuring
Making and using tables
Making and using graphs
Communicating

NOTE: Use *Performance Task Assessment Lists* and *Rubrics* on **pages 89–178** to evaluate student work.

Time Needed This investigation should take approximately one class period.

Preparation For each group, assemble the materials listed on the student page. Use any plant materials that are readily available in your area, making sure to choose natural materials that will have enough genetic variation to be measurable. (Store-bought seeds may not have much variation, since they may be graded and sold by size and they may be bred to be uniform in size.)

Students may work in pairs to do Steps 1 through 5, but the graphing and summary writing should be done individually.

Monitoring the Investigation Remind students that you want to review their hypotheses and approve their procedures and data tables before they continue. After students' procedures and data tables are approved, monitor their work and respond to questions and procedural requests. Encourage students to choose different traits to examine so that they can compare and discuss the variations once their measurements are done.

Expected Outcomes

Step 1

Hypotheses probably will state that certain differences exist among individuals within a species.

Step 2

Students might measure length, width, weight, or another factor.

Step 5

Students should understand that the more data they have to work with, the more reliable their results will be.

Step 6

Graphs probably will have measurements on the horizontal axis and number of individuals on the vertical axis. Some graphs may show a bell-shaped distribution.

Step 7

Students' answers and written paragraphs should agree with their data.

Going Further Students may choose a trait that can be measured, such as height, or a trait that easily can be observed, such as attached or detached earlobes.

Performance Assessment 3

Party Preparations p. 59

Processes and Concepts In conducting this investigation, students may use the following concepts and processes:

- Observing
- Comparing and contrasting
- Recognizing cause and effect
- Controlling variables
- Using controls
- Making tables
- Interpreting data

NOTE: Use *Performance Task Assessment Lists* and *Rubrics* on **pages 89–178** to evaluate student work.

Time Needed This investigation should take approximately two class periods to complete.

Preparation To prepare algal cultures, put some aquarium water in front of a light for a few days. It soon will become green with algae. Algae also may be collected from streams and ponds in your area. Single-celled algae can be found on the surface of a pond. Filamentous algae can be collected using forceps or by scraping rocks.

Algae can be cultured in a jar by adding 1 mL of one percent fertilizer solution to 1 L of pond water. Cover the jar with plastic wrap and leave under a light source. The cultures will become bright green after a few days. Subcultures need to be made every two to three weeks by adding 100 mL of the existing algal culture and 10 mL of the one percent fertilizer solution to 900 mL of distilled water in another jar.

The one percent fertilizer solution is made by adding 1 g of commercial fertilizer (5-10-5) to 100 mL of distilled water. Stir well and store in the refrigerator until needed.

Algicide (100 mL per class) may be obtained from a pool supply store. Do not dilute.

Caution: *As with any biological samples and chemicals, warn the students not to taste any of the materials. Laboratory aprons and gloves should be worn.*

Monitoring the Investigation Tell the students that you want to review and approve their plan before they proceed. After the plan is approved, monitor the work of the students and respond to questions and procedural requests. Remind students to keep a control for comparison of results.

Expected Outcomes A sample student procedure may be as follows:

1. Make a data table to record your observations.
2. Label five test tubes using the numbers 1–5.
3. Fill each test tube half full with the algal culture.
4. Describe the algal culture in a data table.
5. Add the algicide to the test tubes as follows:
   Test tube 1—control; no algicide added
   Test tube 2—add 1 drop of algicide
   Test tube 3—add 5 drops of algicide
   Test tube 4—add 10 drops of algicide
   Test tube 5—add 15 drops of algicide
6. Leave the test tubes in an area with a lot of light.
7. After two days, record your observations. The original green color of the algal culture is still present where the algicide was insufficient to kill the algae. Where the algicide has stopped the growth of the algae and dissolved the cells, the suspensions should become clear.

Going Further Some common household cleaning agents, such as bleach, may be effective as algicides. Soap and mouthwash also may be effective, depending upon the strength of the doses. Drawbacks of using such household chemicals could include: harmful side effects (large doses of bleach are not healthy for your skin or good for bathing suits), expense, less effective than algicide, and so forth.

Performance Assessment 4

Roots or Leaves? p. 61

Processes and Concepts In conducting this investigation, students may use the following concepts and processes:

Observing
Inferring
Hypothesizing
Designing an experiment
Collecting and organizing data
Analyzing data
Making and using tables
Communicating

NOTE: Use *Performance Task Assessment Lists* and *Rubrics* on **pages 89–178** to evaluate student work.

Time Needed This activity should take one class period to set up and another one-half class period to observe and record the results, preferably, the following day.

Preparation You may wish to review the water transportation system in a plant with students, using the illustration on the student page. Bean seeds should be planted about two weeks ahead of time so the seedlings will be 7- to 10-cm tall. Try to choose plants that are as similar as possible for each group. Assemble the materials listed on the student page for each group. Sunflower seedlings could be used in place of the bean seedlings.

Students should work in teams of three for the experiment, but summaries should be written individually. The questions in Step 5 could be handled as a class discussion.

Caution: *Safety goggles and gloves should be worn for the investigation. Students should be reminded that scalpels are sharp and must be handled with care.*

Monitoring the Investigation Tell the students that you want to review their hypotheses and approve their procedures and data tables before they continue. After students' procedures and data tables are approved, monitor their work and respond to questions. Let students determine their own approaches for solving the problem.

Expected Outcomes

Step 1

A hypothesis could state that a plant can or cannot take up water if it is missing its roots. A related hypothesis would state that a plant can or cannot take up water if it is missing its leaves.

Step 2

Students may follow the illustration on the student page for setting up their experiments, or they may try another approach. They will need to include a seedling that lacks leaves and one that lacks roots. They also will need to include a control to show how much water a seedling can take up if it still has both its roots and its leaves. A test tube that contains only water will allow them to compare how much water in the test tube is lost directly to evaporation. Students may use foil to seal the tops of the test tubes to lessen evaporation.

Step 4

Students may observe and measure a change in water level in the test tubes from the starting time to the ending time (perhaps 24 hours later) and record the information in a data table.

Step 6

Written summaries of the findings should agree with student observations and should state whether the hypothesis is supported or not. Most students will observe that plants that still have their leaves will take up the most water. Discuss the importance of transpiration in water transport in plants.

Going Further Students probably will say that they would expect that even more water would be taken up by plants with more leaves. Some students may know that this is caused by an increased water loss (transpiration) through the increased number of leaves.

Performance Assessment 5

Green Mail p. 63

Processes and Concepts In conducting this investigation, students may use the following concepts and processes:

Brainstorming
Using a graphic organizer
Writing a letter
Interpreting data
Recognizing cause and effect

NOTE: Use *Performance Task Assessment Lists* and *Rubrics* on **pages 89–178** to evaluate student work.

Time Needed Use one class period for students to brainstorm and select a global or local environmental problem. Allow students a week or more to conduct research and make a graphic organizer. Have students complete first drafts in class. Devote one class period to sharing letters. Final drafts can be assigned as homework.

Preparation The list of problems provided in the student text is only a starting point. You may wish to have your school media specialist prepare information sources on environmental problems for students to use in their research.

No special materials are required for this task.

Monitoring the Investigation Approve each student's choice of topic. Set a deadline for research notes and submission of a graphic organizer. While this is an individual task, students should read the drafts of their letters to one another for feedback so that subsequent drafts will be more effective.

Organize students into groups of four or five so they can read their letters to a small audience. Have each group select which letters to send to the local newspaper for possible publication. Encourage students to make constructive suggestions for letter revisions. You may wish to model constructive and nonconstructive criticism for students.

Expected Outcomes Each student should have organized research notes on the topic and a graphic organizer displaying how the information fits together. Have students turn in a first and a final draft of the letter, along with the graphic organizer. Students are expected to make convincing and informed arguments for solutions to the problem.

Going Further Help students organize their letters into an informative booklet. You may need to help students group letters into general topics. Local manufacturers and environmental organizations may be willing to underwrite publication and distribution of the booklet. Guide students as they research funding sources and write solicitation letters.

Performance Assessment 6

Choosy Pill Bugs p. 64

Processes and Concepts In conducting this investigation, students may use the following concepts and processes:

- Observing
- Predicting
- Classifying
- Identifying variables
- Designing an experiment
- Hypothesizing
- Making tables
- Controlling variables

NOTE: Use *Performance Task Assessment Lists* and *Rubrics* on **pages 89–178** to evaluate student work.

Time Needed Twenty minutes is needed to discuss and choose test materials the day before the investigation. Allow two days for completing this investigation.

Preparation Pill bugs may be found around your school property under rotting wood and leaves. If you or your students are unable to locate any, they may be purchased from a biological supply house.

Make sure your students choose their test materials before the day of the actual investigation.

Caution: *When working with any living organism, it is extremely important to handle the test organism with great care so that no harm will come to it. The pill bug container must be kept moist, not wet. The containers also must be covered with plastic wrap to prevent escape. All materials used should not be so sticky as to trap the pill bugs. Students should wear gloves, aprons, and goggles.*

Monitoring the Investigation Tell the students you want to review and approve their experiment design and test materials. Discuss the appropriateness of their materials. Remember to point out that their choice of test materials must be specific enough to only test the variable they are questioning.

Encourage your students to choose test materials that mimic some of the conditions that pill bugs may encounter in their natural environment.

After their experimental design is approved, monitor the work of the students, and respond to questions and procedural requests. While trying not to direct the students into any one fixed approach, remind them that the safety of the pill bugs comes first.

Ask students if the test materials they used in this activity represent anything their pill bugs might encounter in their natural environment. Have them give reasons for their answers.

Expected Outcomes This investigation examines the preference of pill bugs. Ask students if the results of their experiments supported their hypotheses. If the students' hypotheses were not supported or their data were inconclusive, look for the students' reasoning processes to explain the results.

Sample Hypothesis: My pill bugs will choose wet sand over dry sand. Because pill bugs have gill-like structures for breathing, they will prefer a moist place to live in.

Yes, the results supported my hypothesis. At the end of the period, 15 of the 18 pill bugs were at the site of the wet sand. The next day, 17 pill bugs were there.

My experiment's results were inconclusive. Ten of the 18 pill bugs were at the site of the wet sand the second day.

Step 5

Sample Experimental Design:

1. Place test materials on opposite sides of a container.
2. Put pill bugs in the middle of the container, halfway between the two test material sites.
3. Leave the pill bugs undisturbed.
4. At the end of the period, record how many pill bugs are at each material site.
5. Leave the pill bugs undisturbed overnight.
6. The next day, record how many pill bugs are at each material site.

Going Further Assist students in selecting the types of test materials that will better reflect the question they are investigating.

Performance Assessment 7

How sweet are you? p. 66

Processes and Concepts In conducting this investigation, students may use the following concepts and processes:

Observing
Designing an experiment
Comparing
Controlling variables
Interpreting data
Making and using tables
Making and using graphs
Measuring
Inferring
Communicating

NOTE: Use *Performance Task Assessment Lists* and *Rubrics* on **pages 89–178** to evaluate student work.

Time Needed This investigation should take one class period to complete, although a second class period may be needed for sharing and graphing data.

Preparation Prior to this investigation, identify any students who have diabetes or experience allergic reaction/sensitivity to sugar, and make sure they do not participate as tasters.

Prepare the original 5.0 percent sugar solution by measuring out 100 g of granulated sugar. Make up to 2 L using water. Stir well.

Let the students work in groups of four. Stress the importance of cleanliness and proper health procedures.

In order to evaluate the class results with any confidence, the different groups must investigate this problem using the same procedure. They also must use the same dilutions to allow for easy class data compilation and comparison. A $\frac{1}{4}$-cup measuring cup from home may be used instead of the 250-mL beaker.

Students can make dilutions by adding $\frac{1}{4}$-cup of the original sugar solution (5.0 percent) to $\frac{1}{4}$-cup of water. The sugar solution is now 2.5 percent. Subsequent dilutions will yield solutions of 1.25 percent, 0.625 percent, and so forth.

Caution: *Stress the importance of cleanliness during this investigation. Be sure that all items being used by the tasting subjects are thoroughly clean and that, upon use, they are immediately cleaned or disposed of.*

Between taste tests, have the students swallow small amounts of water to remove the sweet taste from their mouths. Do not have them spit into sinks or other receptacles.

Monitoring the Investigation Tell the students you want to review and approve their plans before they proceed. Make sure the students use the same dilutions of the sugar solution. If the same dilutions are used, class compilation and comparison can be made.

After the plan is approved, monitor the work of the students and respond to questions and procedural requests. Take notice that all safety procedures are followed. Try to stress independent testing. Caution students against immediate comparison among subjects being tested. While circulating among students, ask them where on their tongues they are tasting the sugar.

Expected Outcomes The students must come up with one procedure to follow. It may be similar to the following procedure.

1. Have subject taste a small amount of the 5.0 percent sugar solution.
2. Record whether or not subject detected a "sweet" taste.
3. Allow subject small mouthfuls of water to remove the sweet taste from his or her mouth. Have subject swallow this water.
4. Dilute the sugar solution. Add $\frac{1}{4}$ cup of the original sugar solution to $\frac{1}{4}$ cup of water. Stir well. The sugar solution is now 2.5 percent. Have subject taste this new solution. Record his or her response.
5. Continue halving the dilution until no sweet taste is detected.

Going Further The students may use dilutions of salt and lemon juice for further investigation.

Performance Assessment 8

The Care and Watering of an Exotic Plant p. 68

Processes and Concepts In conducting this investigation, students may use the following concepts and processes:

Observing
Inferring
Hypothesizing
Designing an experiment
Collecting and organizing data
Analyzing data
Measuring
Making and using tables
Communicating

NOTE: Use *Performance Task Assessment Lists* and *Rubrics* on **pages 89–178** to evaluate student work.

Time Needed This investigation should take approximately one class period.

Preparation For each group, assemble the materials listed on the student page. Each group will need approximately 600 mL of room-temperature water. Room-temperature water can be prepared by filling a large container of water the day before the activity. Each group will need approximately 400 mL of cold water that has been refrigerated for 24 hours or more.

Students may work in groups of two to four to do Steps 1 through 5. The writing of lab reports in Step 6 should be done individually.

Caution: *Students should be reminded to handle glassware carefully. Keeping glassware away from the edges of work areas will help minimize accidents. Remind them not to use thermometers for stirring.*

Monitoring the Investigation Tell the students that you want to review and approve their procedures and data tables before they continue. After students' procedures and data tables are approved, monitor their work and respond to questions. You should not direct the students to use any particular approach.

Expected Outcomes Students' hypotheses and procedures should describe the measurement of the temperature of 100 mL of room-temperature water, the measurement of the temperature of varying amount (less than 100 mL) of cold water, the combining of the room-temperature and the cold water by stirring, and the measurement of the temperature of the mixture. Measurements and calculations should be recorded in a data table. Data tables probably will look similar to the following:

Test	Temperature before mixing (°C)	Temperature after mixing (°C)	Volume (mL)
1	Room temperature	Cold	100
2	Room temperature	Cold	100
3	Room temperature	Cold	100

Have students look at their data tables to determine the best method. The lab report should show that students were able to transfer the knowledge they gained in Step 2 to the care of their plant.

Going Further Students may know, or will be able to find out with a bit of research, that plants also have specific requirements for light, room temperature, and fertilization.

Table of Contents

Performance Task Assessment Lists and Rubrics

Performance Task Assessment Lists and Rubrics

Students perform numerous tasks when completing science education assignments. This section provides checklists—Performance Task assessment Lists—that outline the elements or steps of the tasks identified. These lists facilitate the judging of the quality of the methods used to complete the given tasks as well as the quality of the final product.

Rubrics for the given tasks follow each list. The Rubrics each provide a continuum of quality rating (ranging from poor to excellent) suitable for judging the overall quality of the final product.

The Performance Task Assessment Lists may be used as published in this book, or they may be tailored to specific tasks. Shortening the lists, combining them with other lists, or rewording them may allow clearer communication with a particular group of students. You may wish to prepare Performance Task Assessment Lists and Rubrics for other products and processes that you identify, following the model of those included in this book.

PERFORMANCE TASK ASSESSMENT LIST

Making Observations and Inferences

Element	Assessment Points: Points Possible	Earned Assessment: Self	Earned Assessment: Teacher
Making Observations			
1. Observations are made safely using all appropriate senses.	_____	_____	_____
2. Observations are quantitatively accurate and use metric measurements appropriately.	_____	_____	_____
3. Observations are qualitatively accurate.	_____	_____	_____
4. When necessary, scientific drawings are made. (See Performance Task Assessment List for Scientific Drawing p. 127))	_____	_____	_____
5. Appropriate tools and materials are used to make observations.	_____	_____	_____
6. Personal opinions, conclusions, or inferences are avoided while making observations.	_____	_____	_____
7. Data are recorded and organized appropriately and neatly. (See Performance Task Assessment List for Data Table p. 109)	_____	_____	_____
Making Inferences			
8. Inferences are reasonable given the observations made and the observer's prior knowledge.	_____	_____	_____
9. Inferences are explained and justified based on the observer's prior knowledge.	_____	_____	_____
Total	_____	_____	_____

RUBRIC

Making Observations and Inferences

	Rating
The student provides a highly organized list of quantitative (mathematical calculations) and qualitative (informed judgments) observations, showing that a major effort went into the study. Very impressive drawings and diagrams are made to accompany the data. Carefully thought-out inferences are made and justified by the observations and by prior knowledge.	
The student makes detailed observations using all the appropriate senses safely. Both quantitative and qualitative observations are made accurately. The student shows skill in using tools and materials. Drawings or diagrams are carefully drawn to accompany the data. The student records observations without making opinions, conclusions, or inferences. The records kept are organized and easy to read. Thoughtful inferences are made and justified based on the observations and on the student's prior knowledge.	
The student makes incomplete and/or inaccurate observations. The metric system is not used appropriately. The student did not use the tools or equipment well. Drawings or diagrams are missing, or they are poorly done. The list of observations is not well organized and/or it contains personal opinions, conclusions, or inferences. When inferences are made, they are not thoughtfully justified based on the observations and/or on the student's prior knowledge.	
The work is very poorly done or has not been completed.	

Note: For drawings, use the Performance Task Assessment List for Scientific Drawings.

Comments:

PERFORMANCE TASK ASSESSMENT LIST

Asking Questions

Element	Points Possible	Self	Teacher
		Assessment Points Earned Assessment	
1. Thoughtful and relevant questions are asked.	______	______	______
2. Questions are well-crafted.	______	______	______
3. Questions emerge logically from the observations made.	______	______	______
4. Questions are descriptive.	______	______	______
5. Questions interpret the observations.	______	______	______
6. Questions analyze the observations.	______	______	______
7. Questions lead to observations.	______	______	______
8. Questions lead to reasonable predictions.	______	______	______
9. A question is selected for investigation.	______	______	______
10. A thoughtful justification is given for why that question has been selected for further study.	______	______	______
Total	______	______	______

RUBRIC

Asking Questions

	Rating
The student shows great insight by crafting superb and very interesting questions. Higher-order thinking is clear. The student gives mostly thoughtful explanations as to why a particular question has been selected for further study.	
The student asks many questions that exhibit a thoughtful consideration of the observations. Questions include higher-order thinking, such as interpretation, analysis, synthesis, and evaluation. The questions lead directly to predictions that can become the basis for experiments. The student offers a clear explanation for why a particular question has been chosen for further study.	
The list of questions shows little effort. Higher-order thinking is not evident. Some questions do not seem to be related to the observations. The student does not give a thoughtful explanation as to why a particular question has been selected for further study.	
The work is very poorly done or has not been completed.	

Comments:

PERFORMANCE TASK ASSESSMENT LIST

Formulating a Hypothesis

Element	Assessment Points: Points Possible	Earned Assessment: Self	Earned Assessment: Teacher
1. The hypothesis is a simple statement that reflects the observations.	______	______	______
2. Predictions result from the hypothesis.	______	______	______
3. A thoughtful justification is made for why the hypothesis and its more specific prediction can serve as the basis for an experiment.	______	______	______
4. The predictions are useful in designing the experiment.	______	______	______
Total	______	______	______

RUBRIC

Formulating a Hypothesis

	Rating
The student makes a remarkably insightful hypothesis. The prediction is clearly testable, and the student provides a thoughtful explanation of how the hypothesis and prediction will provide the basis for designing an excellent experiment.	
The student makes a clear, declarative hypothesis statement, which is followed by a prediction that relates the independent variable (what the experimenter changes) to the dependent variable (how the thing responds). It is evident how the hypothesis and prediction flow from the observations. The student justifies how the hypothesis and prediction provide the basis for designing an experiment.	
The hypothesis is not clear, nor is the prediction. It is not clear how the hypothesis and prediction flow from the observations. The student does not offer a thoughtful explanation as to how the hypothesis and prediction will provide the basis for designing an experiment.	
The work is very poorly done or has not been completed.	

Comments:

PERFORMANCE TASK ASSESSMENT LIST

Designing an Experiment

Element	Assessment Points: Points Possible	Earned Assessment: Self	Earned Assessment: Teacher
1. The experimental design tests the prediction.			
2. The statement of the problem explains the need for the experiment.			
3. The methods and procedures used in the experiment follow a sequence.			
4. The experimental procedure is complete and clear enough that another person could carry it out.			
5. An appropriate independent variable is clearly identified.			
6. The plan allows for the independent variable to be controlled and measured accurately.			
7. An appropriate dependent variable is clearly identified.			
8. The plan allows for the dependent variable to be measured accurately.			
9. The experimental design uses the metric system wherever possible.			
10. The experiment includes proper controls.			
11. Margin of "error" is noted.			
12. A complete list of required materials is provided.			
13. An appropriate strategy to use repeated trials and measurements is described.			
14. Experimental design includes appropriate safety concerns.			
15. The experimental write-up is neat and well-organized.			
16. Appropriate vocabulary, language mechanics, and complete sentences are used.			
17. Instructions are provided for proper clean-up and disposal of wastes.			
Total			

RUBRIC

Designing an Experiment

	Rating
The experiment is exemplary in its clarity and completeness and shows an understanding of the process. It has the potential to provide data that can be used to evaluate the hypothesis and its prediction. The sequence of steps is excellent. The student shows a clear understanding of the need for controls, the need to replicate the experiment, and the need for strategies to minimize error. All safety and workstation precautions are thoughtfully planned.	
The experiment clearly tests the prediction. The sequence of steps is complete in that another person could follow it. The independent and dependent variables are appropriately chosen, and the student thoughtfully plans how to control and measure them. The student plans to use tools and materials. The student shows a good understanding of the need for controls, the need to replicate the experiment, and the need for strategies to minimize error. Safety precautions are planned, as are strategies to deal with the care of the workstation and disposal of wastes.	
The plan is incomplete and/or disorganized. The independent and/or dependent variables are not well-chosen, and/or the plans for measuring them are not well-developed. No clear understanding of controls and/or the need for replicating the experiment is evident. The student has not described strategies to minimize error. Safety precautions are lacking or are incomplete. Plans to care for the workstation and dispose of wastes are lacking or incomplete.	
The work is very poorly done or has not been completed.	

Comments:

PERFORMANCE TASK ASSESSMENT LIST

Carrying Out a Strategy and Collecting Data

Element	Assessment Points: Points Possible	Assessment Points: Earned Assessment — Self	Assessment Points: Earned Assessment — Teacher
1. Appropriate tools and materials are selected to collect the data.	______	______	______
2. Skill in using the tools and materials to collect accurate data is demonstrated.	______	______	______
3. Repeated measurements are taken and recorded.	______	______	______
4. Tools are used safely and properly.	______	______	______
5. Tools and materials are put away properly and the work area is cleaned.	______	______	______
6. Strategies are used to minimize error.	______	______	______
Total	______	______	______

RUBRIC

Carrying Out a Strategy and Collecting Data

	Rating
The student shows great skill in carrying out the experiment. Safety precautions are excellent. The experiment is replicated and error is carefully minimized. The work-station and materials clean up, along with disposal, are thoughtfully done.	
The student follows the procedure for carrying out the experiment. The student selects and shows skill in safely using proper tools, equipment, and materials to carry out the procedure. The experiment is replicated, and strategies to minimize error are employed. The workstation is cleaned, and materials and tools are put away properly. Wastes are disposed of properly.	
The student does not follow the procedure completely. Little skill is shown in using the tools, equipment, and materials. The experiment is not replicated, and/or error is not kept to a reasonable minimum. The workstation is not cleaned properly. Tools, equipment, and materials are not put away properly. Wastes are not disposed of properly.	
The work is very poorly done or has not been completed.	

Comments:

PERFORMANCE TASK ASSESSMENT LIST

Analyzing the Data

Element	Assessment Points: Points Possible	Assessment Points: Earned Assessment — Self	Assessment Points: Earned Assessment — Teacher
1. The analysis includes all the data.	______	______	______
2. The analysis includes appropriate statistical procedures.	______	______	______
3. The analysis is accurate and thoughtful.	______	______	______
Total	______	______	______

RUBRIC

Analyzing the Data

	Rating
The student makes an excellent analysis and shows great insight. Math is used correctly in the analysis.	
The student makes use of all the data in the analysis and the student correctly uses the appropriate mathematical procedures in analyzing it.	
The analysis does not make use of all the data. The statistical procedures used are not appropriate or they are not accurately carried out.	
The work is very poorly done or has not been completed.	

Comments:

PERFORMANCE TASK ASSESSMENT LIST

Using Math in Science

Element	Assessment Points: Points Possible	Earned Assessment: Self	Earned Assessment: Teacher
Understanding the Problem			
1. The problem is clearly defined by being restated.	______	______	______
2. Given information is identified.	______	______	______
3. Information that must be assumed is listed.	______	______	______
4. Information that must be obtained is listed.	______	______	______
5. A clear diagram is drawn that shows the important elements of the problem.	______	______	______
Solving the Problem			
6. The algebraic formula(s) for this problem is listed.	______	______	______
7. The formula(s) is rearranged correctly to solve for the unknown quantity.	______	______	______
8. Appropriately labeled values are put in the final formula.	______	______	______
9. Appropriate arithmetic operations are used accurately.	______	______	______
10. All values are labeled.	______	______	______
11. Reasoning can be easily followed by the sequence of arithmetic operations.	______	______	______
12. The appropriate number of significant figures is used.	______	______	______
13. Scientific notation is correctly used.	______	______	______
14. The answer is correct and labeled correctly.	______	______	______
15. The answer is appropriate according to the assumptions and reasoning used.	______	______	______
Communicating the Result			
16. A clear, concise statement of the problem, the strategy for the solution, and the answer are made. Math vocabulary is used correctly.	______	______	______
17. A labeled diagram is used to support the written statement.	______	______	______
Total	______	______	______

RUBRIC

Using Math in Science

	Rating
The student shows an especially thoughtful analysis of the problem and selects the correct formulas to solve the problem effectively. The work is organized, complete, and very easy to follow. The answer is superbly communicated to the audience with the correct labels and significant figures.	
The student shows that he or she understands the problem by paraphrasing it, identifying information that is given and that which must be estimated or assumed, and drawing a diagram to show the problem more clearly. The student uses formulas well to solve the problem. The answers are accurate, include correct unit labels, and have an appropriate number of significant figures. The student communicates the answer in an understandable way to the intended audience so that the audience is confident that the student is skilled at math problem solving.	
The student shows little understanding of the problem. The solution is faulty, incorrect formulas are used, and the answer is inaccurate. The answer is not communicated effectively to the intended audience.	
The work is very poorly done or has not been completed.	

Comments:

PERFORMANCE TASK ASSESSMENT LIST

Evaluating a Hypothesis

Element	Assessment Points: Points Possible	Earned Assessment: Self	Earned Assessment: Teacher
1. A clear statement is made about whether or not the hypothesis and the more specific prediction are supported.	______	______	______
2. The evaluation of the hypothesis and prediction is justified.	______	______	______
3. Inferences and extrapolations may be made but are clearly separated from conclusions based on the data and their analysis.	______	______	______
Total	______	______	______

RUBRIC

Evaluating a Hypothesis

	Rating
The student makes a very clear statement of the hypothesis and justifies it in a most analytical manner. The justification for the hypothesis and prediction are clearly supported. Any inferences or estimations show highly thoughtful insights. The conclusions are completely supported by the data.	
The student makes and supports a clear statement about whether or not the hypothesis and the specific prediction are supported. The justification ties the data and its analysis to the conclusion. If inferences or extrapolations (estimates) are made, they are clearly identified as such and not confused with conclusions supported by data and its analysis.	
The student does not make a clear statement as to whether or not the hypothesis and the specific prediction are supported. Little justification is made for any conclusion reached. Inferences or estimations made are confused with conclusions supported by the data and its analysis.	
The work is very poorly done or has not been completed.	

Comments:

PERFORMANCE TASK ASSESSMENT LIST

Assessing a Whole Experiment and Planning the Next Experiment

Element	Points Possible	Earned Assessment: Self	Earned Assessment: Teacher
1. Strengths and weaknesses of the whole experiment are identified.	______	______	______
2. Sources of error are identified.	______	______	______
3. Applicable strategies are suggested for reducing errors.	______	______	______
4. Questions that have arisen during the experiment are stated that could provide the focus for further investigations.	______	______	______
5. A question is selected to use as the focus for the next experiment.	______	______	______
Total	______	______	______

RUBRIC

Assessing a Whole Experiment and Planning the Next Experiment

	Rating
The student shows great insight and thoughtful work in revisiting the experiment to identify its strengths and to find ways to improve it, including strategies to reduce error. A thoughtful list of questions for future study is made, and the student has selected a question for the next experiment. A clear justification is made as to why that particular question should be investigated next.	
The student revisits the whole experiment and identifies strengths of the work and areas for improvement. Understanding of the types of errors is evident. The student proposes strategies to improve the experiment. The student lists questions that have arisen during the experiment which could be the basis for future experiments. A question is selected for future study and this selection is justified.	
The student shows little thought in reviewing the experiment and finding its strengths and need for improvement. Understanding how error enters into the experiment is not evident. Few, if any, suggestions are made to improve the experiment. The student lists few, if any, questions for further study.	
The work is very poorly done or has not been completed.	

Comments:

PERFORMANCE TASK ASSESSMENT LIST

Conducting a Survey and Graphing the Results

Element	Assessment Points: Points Possible	Earned Assessment: Self	Earned Assessment: Teacher
1. The topic or question to be researched is clearly stated.	______	______	______
2. The population to be surveyed is appropriate to the topic or question.	______	______	______
3. Questions on the survey are clearly stated for the understanding of those being surveyed.	______	______	______
4. The survey questions are relevant to the topic or question.	______	______	______
5. The plan to collect data is prepared thoughtfully so that the data will be valid and reliable.	______	______	______
6. The data from the survey are organized and labeled.	______	______	______
7. The appropriate type of graph is used for the data and the audience. (See Performance Task Assessment List for Graph from Data p. 111)	______	______	______
Total	______	______	______

RUBRIC

Conducting a Survey and Graphing the Results

	Rating
The survey is masterfully conceived. The population to be surveyed has been carefully chosen and the strategy to conduct the survey is valid and reliable. The graph is eye-catching and is very easy to understand. All graphing techniques are excellent. Data from the survey is organized into a clearly labeled chart or table. A key is present and easy to understand.	
The question or topic for the survey is appropriate to the assignment and has been stated concisely. The population to be surveyed has been chosen, and the strategy to conduct the survey will provide valid and reliable data. Data from the survey are organized into a labeled chart or table. The data have been accurately represented in an appropriate type of graph, which has clear labels and a title. The graph uses space, color, textures, and other visual techniques well, making it interesting and easy to understand. A key is present.	
The survey question or topic is not clear nor is it on target, according to the assignment. The strategies to select a population and implement the survey are faulty and will yield data that are not valid or reliable. Data from the survey are not well organized. An incorrect or inappropriate graph format has been used. The titles, labels, and/or units are missing, unclear, or inaccurate. The graph appears unorganized, too crowded, and/or sloppy.	
The work is very poorly done or has not been completed.	

Comments:

PERFORMANCE TASK ASSESSMENT LIST

Data Table

Element	Assessment Points: Points Possible	Earned Assessment: Self	Earned Assessment: Teacher
1. The data table includes the appropriate data.	______	______	______
2. An appropriate title for the data table is provided.	______	______	______
3. The information in the data table columns is appropriately organized and labeled.	______	______	______
4. Units of measurement for all variables are clearly indicated.	______	______	______
5. Data for the independent and dependent variables are clearly shown.	______	______	______
6. The data have an appropriate number of significant figures.	______	______	______
7. Accuracy of the data is appropriate to the measuring equipment or instrument being used.	______	______	______
8. Data from multiple trials at each level of the independent variable are clearly shown.	______	______	______
9. The data table is neat and presentable.	______	______	______
Total	______	______	______

RUBRIC

Data Table

	Rating
The student's data table is exceptionally well organized, clear, and concise. The accuracy of the data collected from the measuring equipment or instruments being used was excellent. The data show an understanding of the procedures involved. The table is neat and presentable.	
The student's data table is good. The accuracy of the data collected from the measuring equipment or instruments is satisfactory. The data show a basic understanding of the procedures involved.	
The student's data table shows inaccuracies related to the measuring equipment or instruments used. The data show some problems related to the procedure involved. The table is unorganized and not done neatly.	
The work is very poorly done or has not been completed.	

Comments:

PERFORMANCE TASK ASSESSMENT LIST

Graph from Data

Element	Assessment Points: Points Possible	Earned Assessment: Self	Earned Assessment: Teacher
1. An appropriate type of graph is used.	______	______	______
2. Appropriate starting points and intervals are used for each axis.	______	______	______
3. An appropriate scale is used on each axis depending on the range of data for that axis.	______	______	______
4. There is a main title for the graph, which clearly states the relationship between the axes.	______	______	______
5. Axes are clearly labeled.	______	______	______
6. The independent variable is put on the *x*-axis and the dependent variable is put on the *y*-axis.	______	______	______
7. The data are plotted accurately.	______	______	______
8. The graph should reflect any uncertainty of measurement.	______	______	______
9. Trends or lack of trends are indicated on the graph.	______	______	______
10. Colors, textures, labels, or other features are employed to make the graph easier to read.	______	______	______
11. If necessary, a key is given.	______	______	______
12. The graph is neat and presentable.	______	______	______
Total	______	______	______

RUBRIC

Graph from Data

	Rating
The student's graph is outstanding in its ability to clearly and easily convey accurate information. Variables are put on the correct axes and labeled accurately. The graph shows excellent use of space with all data plotted correctly. All parts of the graph are accurately labeled. A clear key is presented. The graph is very neat and presentable.	
The student selects an appropriate type of graph for the data. The variables are put on the correct axes, which are accurately labeled. An appropriate scale with reasonable starting points and intervals is used on each axis so that the graph fits the space allotted well. The data is plotted correctly. The title is clear and describes the two variables. The graph is neat, presentable, and easy to read. A key is present.	
The student chooses an inappropriate or incorrect type of graph. The variables are put on the wrong axes. The axes are not labeled or are labeled inadequately. The scales are not appropriate, and the lines or bars do not fit the space well. The title is missing or inadequate. The graph is not easy to read or understand. The key is missing or inadequate.	
The work is very poorly done or has not been completed.	

Comments:

PERFORMANCE TASK ASSESSMENT LIST

Written Summary of a Graph

Element	Assessment Points: Points Possible	Earned Assessment: Self	Earned Assessment: Teacher
1. The summary gives a reasonable interpretation of the data.	_____	_____	_____
2. The research question is answered from the results based on the data.	_____	_____	_____
3. There is reference to both independent and dependent variables.	_____	_____	_____
4. The relationship between the dependent and the independent variables is clearly and accurately described.	_____	_____	_____
5. The summary is concise.	_____	_____	_____
6. Appropriate vocabulary, grammar, and complete sentences are used.	_____	_____	_____
7. The summary is neat and presentable.	_____	_____	_____
Total	_____	_____	_____

RUBRIC

Written Summary of a Graph

	Rating
The student's summary is accurate and precise and uses especially appropriate vocabulary to describe the graph to the intended audience. A clear conclusion about the research question is reached. Any inferences are identified as such.	
The student's summary clearly and accurately states the relationship between independent and dependent variables. A conclusion about the research question is reached. The summary is concise and neat. Language mechanics are excellent.	
The student's summary is inaccurate or unclear in stating the relationship between independent and dependent variables. No conclusion about the research question is clearly reached. The summary mixes statements of fact with inferences. The summary is not well organized, and its language mechanics are not well done.	
The work is very poorly done or has not been completed.	

Comments:

PERFORMANCE TASK ASSESSMENT LIST

Consumer Decision-Making Study

Element	Points Possible	Earned Assessment: Self	Earned Assessment: Teacher
1. A consumer product has been selected to be evaluated. The reason that this type of product was selected is clearly stated.	______	______	______
2. A set of criteria by which to judge the product has been thoughtfully selected.	______	______	______
3. A strategy to collect valid and reliable data on each criteria for each product sample has been clearly and thoughtfully planned.	______	______	______
4. The scientific process is used to collect data for some criteria.	______	______	______
5. A scoring system to assess each criteria has been thoroughly constructed.	______	______	______
6. Sources of error have been considered, and error has been minimized.	______	______	______
7. The data are collected in an organized manner so that they can be used.	______	______	______
8. A final presentation of the data is made in a format that clearly communicates the results of the study.	______	______	______
9. A clear conclusion is reached, and it is supported by data from the research.	______	______	______
Total	______	______	______

RUBRIC

Consumer Decision-Making Study

	Rating
The student's work is superb. It shows much thought in the explanation for why the product was selected. Great care is taken to collect appropriate, valid, and reliable data. The scientific process, where appropriate, is used. The student thoughtfully considers potential sources of error and works to reduce error. The final format to display the findings is creative and extremely clear. The presentation uses a format that communicates the findings in an excellent manner to the intended audience.	
The student selects a consumer product to assess and provides a clear explanation for why that product was selected. The student plans a strategy to collect valid and reliable data on each criterion for each sample of the product. The student uses the scientific method where appropriate. The student considers potential sources of error and works to reduce error. The data collected are organized in a useful manner. The final presentation of the data uses a format that clearly conveys the results of the tests to the intended audience.	
The student does not provide a clear explanation for why the product was selected for assessment. The set of criteria selected to test each sample is inadequate and/or inappropriate. The strategy is not adequate to collect valid or reliable data. The scientific method selected is inadequate. The data collected is poorly organized. Sources of error are not thoughtfully considered and/or controlled. The final format used to present the data and findings is unclear and/or incomplete.	
The work is very poorly done or has not been completed.	

Comments:

PERFORMANCE TASK ASSESSMENT LIST

Invention

Element	Assessment Points: Points Possible	Earned Assessment: Self	Earned Assessment: Teacher
1. The problem or need for which the invention is a solution is clearly stated.	_____	_____	_____
2. A design for the invention shows its dimensions and parts. Metric measurement is used whenever possible.	_____	_____	_____
3. An explanation of the design describes how the parts function and what materials will be used to make the invention.	_____	_____	_____
4. The invention works to perform its intended function very well.	_____	_____	_____
5. The invention is durable and functions reliably.	_____	_____	_____
6. The invention is safe.	_____	_____	_____
7. The invention gets a high green rating for its friendliness to the environment.	_____	_____	_____
8. The invention is attractive and appealing to those who would use it.	_____	_____	_____
9. The invention is original or is an improvement to a previous invention.	_____	_____	_____
10. The written directions for the invention are clear and easy to follow.	_____	_____	_____
Total	_____	_____	_____

RUBRIC

Invention

	Rating
The student's invention is remarkably creative and clearly solves a problem or meets the need for which it is intended. The plan for the invention is of high technical quality. The invention works extremely well and is attractive, safe, sturdy, and reliable. It is made and used with great respect for the environment. The set of directions written for the invention is extremely clear and easy to follow.	
The student clearly describes the problem or need for which the invention provides a solution. The student makes a clear and neat plan that shows the dimensions and parts of the invention. Metric measurement is used. The plan also shows how the parts work and of what materials the invention is made. The actual invention is safe and works well and reliably to perform its intended function. It is made and used with respect for the environment. A set of complete and easy-to-follow directions accompany it.	
The student does not define the problem or need for which the invention provides a solution. The plan for the invention is incomplete. It does not show the dimensions accurately or completely. It does not clearly show the parts and/or how they work. The actual invention does not work well. The invention is not completely environmentally friendly. The set of instructions is missing, incomplete, or difficult to follow.	
The invention is a copy, does not work, or has not been completed. There are no instructions for the invention.	

Comments:

PERFORMANCE TASK ASSESSMENT LIST

Lab Report

Element	Assessment Points: Points Possible	Earned Assessment: Self	Earned Assessment: Teacher
Introduction			
1. The title states clearly the independent and dependent variable (without stating what the effect actually is).	______	______	______
2. Name(s) of experimenters(s) is/are given.	______	______	______
3. A concise summary of the project includes the statement of the problem, the hypothesis, the procedures, the main results, and the conclusions. (Not to exceed 250 words.)			
Statement of the Problem			
4. The background for the problem is summarized.	______	______	______
5. Relevant literature is cited.	______	______	______
6. The hypothesis is stated clearly. It predicts the influence of the independent variable on the dependent variable.	______	______	______
Experimental Design			
7. The procedure for controlling and measuring variables through repeated trials is easy to follow. (See Performance Task Assessment List for Designing an Experiment p. 95)	______	______	______
Data Collection and Display			
8. Refer to the Performance Task Assessment List for Data Table p. 107.	______	______	______
9. Refer to the Performance Task Assessment List for Graph from Data p. 109.	______	______	______
Data Analysis			
10. Refer to the Performance Task Assessment List for Analyzing the Data p. 99.	______	______	______
Conclusion			
11. The hypothesis is evaluated clearly.	______	______	______
12. Extrapolations from the data are made and justified.	______	______	______
13. Connections are made to other studies (if appropriate).	______	______	______
14. Recommendations are made for further study.	______	______	______
Other			
15. The student understands the science behind the study.	______	______	______
16. Language is used correctly.	______	______	______
17. References in the bibliography are made properly.	______	______	______
18. The report is neat and presentable.	______	______	______
Total	______	______	______

RUBRIC

Lab Report

	Rating
The student's report is excellent. It is highly organized and most thoughtfully presented. The statement of the problem includes a description of how the problem was identified, a clear statement of the hypothesis, a more specific prediction of the relationship between the independent and dependent variables (when called for), and a summary of very relevant literature. The overall impression of validity and reliability is strong. It is clear that the student has a masterful control of the scientific process. Language mechanics are excellent and the report is very presentable.	
The student's report includes an introduction that gives the name(s) of the experimenter(s) and the title, and clearly a states the independent and dependent variables (if called for), as well as provides a concise summary of the entire experiment. The statement of the problem includes a description of how the problem was identified, a statement of the hypothesis, and a summary of relevant literature. Data, first organized into charts and/or tables with correct titles and labels, is correctly put into graphs that are very good. It is clear that the student understands the science involved in the experiment and has an excellent command of the scientific process. Language mechanics are good and the report is presentable.	
The student's report includes an introduction that is missing information; the summary also is unclear. In the statement of the problem, the reason the experiment was done is not clear and/or the hypothesis is inappropriate or awkward. The experimental design cannot be duplicated from the information provided and/or there are significant errors in the experimental design. The data is not well-organized and/or it is used incorrectly in graphs that are poorly drawn. The student has a poor mastery of the science concepts and of the scientific procedure. Many errors occur in language mechanics. The report is of low quality.	
The work is very poorly done or has not been completed.	

Comments:

PERFORMANCE TASK ASSESSMENT LIST

Making and Using a Classification System

Element	Assessment Points: Points Possible	Earned Assessment: Self	Earned Assessment: Teacher
1. The characteristics chosen begin with the most general and logically proceed to the most specific.	______	______	______
2. The characteristics chosen are part of the essential nature of the objects being classified.	______	______	______
3. Each criterion in the classification system is specific.	______	______	______
4. Several people can use the classification system with the same set of objects and classify them the same.	______	______	______
5. New objects that are related can be classified using this classification system.	______	______	______
6. The classification system can be modified to work with new objects, which have not been previously classified but are related to the original set.	______	______	______
Total	______	______	______

RUBRIC

Making and Using a Classification System

	Rating
The student's classification system uses characteristics that are essential to the nature of the objects being classified. The decision-making path flows smoothly from general to specific through a logical series of decisions. The classification system is especially easy for others to use. It also works exceptionally well with many new, but related, objects.	
The student's classification system uses characteristics that are necessary to the nature of the objects being classified. The decision-making path flows from general to specific through a logical series of decisions related to specific and concrete characteristics of the objects being classified. Several people, using this classification system independently, classify objects in the same way. The classification system can be used with new objects and can be modified to better fit and expand the collection.	
The student's classification system is only partially useable. Several people using the classification system make some similar decisions, but other classification decisions differ greatly, so that the final result is that they do not classify the objects in the same way.	
The classification system does not work or has not been completed.	

Comments:

PERFORMANCE TASK ASSESSMENT LIST

Model

Element	Assessment Points: Points Possible	Earned Assessment: Self	Earned Assessment: Teacher
1. A clear explanation is made of how the model will demonstrate the science concepts it is intended to show.			
2. A clear plan for the model is drawn. The plan shows dimensions and parts. Metric measurement is used.			
3. The plan includes an explanation of how the model simulates the real item. The explanation includes a description of how the model differs from the real item.			
4. The constructed model is sturdy and simulates the elements of the real item that it was intended to simulate.			
5. Color, labels, and other such devices clarify what the model is intended to show.			
6. The model is neat and presentable.			
7. The model is safe to use.			
Total			

RUBRIC

Model

	Rating
The student's model cleverly and clearly demonstrates the science concept(s) it is intended to show. The plan is of high technical quality. The model does an outstanding job of simulating the elements of the real item it is intended to demonstrate. The model is of very high artistic and technical quality.	
The student describes the science concepts the model is intended to show. It is clear that the student understands the science concepts. The model simulates the elements of the real item it is intended to demonstrate. The constructed model is sturdy and of artistic and technical quality. The model is safe, neat, and presentable.	
The student does not explain the science concepts that the model is intended to show. It is unclear how well the student knows the science concepts. The explanation of how the model is similar to and dissimilar from the real item is incomplete or inaccurate. The constructed model does not work well or at all. The model is unsafe, not neat, nor presentable.	
The model is very inaccurate and poorly done or has not been completed.	

Comments:

PERFORMANCE TASK ASSESSMENT LIST

Science Fair Display

Element	Assessment Points: Points Possible	Assessment Points: Earned Assessment — Self	Assessment Points: Earned Assessment — Teacher
Background			
1. A concise statement of the background for the problem is made clearly.	______	______	______
2. The hypothesis and a prediction are stated clearly.	______	______	______
Procedure			
3. The description of the procedure used is clear and includes the following:	______	______	______
a. identification of independent and dependent variables	______	______	______
b. description of how independent variable was varied and measured	______	______	______
c. description of how dependent variable was measured	______	______	______
d. strategy for keeping other factors constant	______	______	______
e. strategy for having a control	______	______	______
f. strategy for repeated trials	______	______	______
Data			
4. Charts and/or tables are done correctly. (See Performance Task Assessment List for Data Table p. 109)	______	______	______
5. Graphs are done correctly. (See Performance Task Assessment List for Graph from Data p. 111)	______	______	______
6. Data analysis is summarized. (See Performance Task Assessment List for Written Summary of a Graph p. 113)	______	______	______
Conclusion			
7. The major findings are stated clearly.	______	______	______
8. Key points of interpretation are made.	______	______	______
9. Questions for further study are stated.	______	______	______
10. Bibliography page is provided in proper form.	______	______	______
Other			
11. The narratives contain no errors in use of language.	______	______	______
12. Graphics are attractive and legible.	______	______	______
13. Props add to the clarity and interest of the display.	______	______	______
14. The display is informative and attractive.	______	______	______
15. The experimenter answers questions about the experimental design.	______	______	______
16. The experimenter answers questions about the science behind the experiment.	______	______	______
17. All guidelines for the science fair are followed.	______	______	______
Total	______	______	______

RUBRIC

Science Fair Display

	Rating
The student's display is outstanding. It is extremely informative and attractive. It is clear that the student has mastered the science and the scientific processes involved. The statement of the problem, hypothesis, specific predictions, appropriate summary of the explanation of the design, and display of data in charts and/or graphs helps the audience understand the entire experiment within a minute or two of examination.	
The student's display is very eye-catching. It is attractive and all the parts seem to fit together without being crowded. The statement of the problem, hypothesis, prediction, summary of the experimental design, display of the data charts, and/or graphs, and a good evaluation of the hypothesis are organized so that the audience can understand the entire experiment within two or three minutes of examination. It is obvious that the student has a good basic knowledge of the science and scientific processes involved. Elements of the experimental equipment are provided to demonstrate elements and/or results of the experiment. These materials add much interest and help the audience learn more from the display.	
The student's display is unorganized and cluttered. It does not present a clear story of a question, a process, or the resulting data. Some elements of the experimental design are missing or poorly represented. After two or three minutes of study, the audience is still not sure what the student did or what was concluded. There may be flaws in the experimental design. Many mechanical errors exist in the narrative. Overall, the equipment displayed adds little real information for the audience.	
The work is very poorly done or has not been completed.	

Comments:

PERFORMANCE TASK ASSESSMENT LIST

Scientific Drawing

	Assessment Points		
	Points Possible	Earned Assessment	
Element		Self	Teacher
1. Appropriate and accurate details of structure are shown.	______	______	______
2. The drawings show an appropriate number of views of the object so that all of it is represented in the drawings.	______	______	______
3. All drawings use the same scale, which is shown clearly. The scale is metric.	______	______	______
4. Accurate details of color, pattern, texture, and/or other physical characteristics are shown.	______	______	______
5. If appropriate, the relationship of the object to its surroundings is shown and is accurate.	______	______	______
6. If appropriate, the relationship between the structure and function of the object is shown and is accurate.	______	______	______
7. Text accompanies the drawing and explains the science that the drawing is intended to show.	______	______	______
8. Labels are used accurately.	______	______	______
9. Drawings are neat and presentable.	______	______	______
Total	______	______	______

RUBRIC

Scientific Drawing

	Rating
The student's drawing is striking and realistic. The detail is meticulous. A very precise scale is used consistently. The scale uses the metric system. Enough views of the object are drawn to provide the audience with a complete picture of the structure under study. Labels are used to help convey information. The principles of artistic composition are employed well in this drawing.	
The student's drawing shows the details of the structure of the object. The student has drawn the object to a scale which is clearly marked. The metric scale is used. Ample views of the object are drawn to provide the audience with an accurate picture of the structures under study. Labels are used to provide needed information. The drawing is neat and presentable.	
The student's drawing does not show much detail of the structure. The drawing is not done to a consistent scale. The scale is not metric. Details of color, pattern, and texture are not used well. Labels are incorrect or lacking. The drawing is not neat.	
The work is very poorly done or has not been completed.	

Comments:

PERFORMANCE TASK ASSESSMENT LIST

Booklet or Pamphlet

Element	Assessment Points: Points Possible	Earned Assessment: Self	Earned Assessment: Teacher
1. There is a clear theme throughout the booklet or pamphlet.	_____	_____	_____
2. Chapters or sections are organized to support the theme.	_____	_____	_____
3. Chapters or sections have clear main ideas.	_____	_____	_____
4. Main ideas are supported with appropriate information.	_____	_____	_____
5. It is clear that the core concepts relevant to the assignment are understood.	_____	_____	_____
6. Original thinking is clearly evident.	_____	_____	_____
7. Information sources are properly identified.	_____	_____	_____
8. Diagrams, pictures, and other graphics are of quality and add to the overall effectiveness of the booklet or pamphlet.	_____	_____	_____
9. The proper format is followed.	_____	_____	_____
10. Writing is of high quality.	_____	_____	_____
11. The work is very neat and presentable.	_____	_____	_____
12. The work communicates well with the intended audience.	_____	_____	_____
13. The work is creative and interesting.	_____	_____	_____
Total	_____	_____	_____

RUBRIC

Booklet or Pamphlet

	Rating
This student's work is exemplary. There is a clear, focused theme for the entire piece and each component supports it. The supporting details enhance the quality of the main ideas and are masterfully woven into the work. The sources are properly referenced. Proper format is used. There are no mechanical errors.	
This student's work is excellent. There is a focused theme for the entire piece, and each component supports it. The supporting details add to the quality of the main ideas and are woven into the work. They do not appear to be "stuck on" or list-like. Appropriate information from a variety of sources is used and referenced. The proper format is used. There are very few, if any, mechanical errors, none of which interfere with the meaning of the booklet or pamphlet.	
The student's work is weak. It does not accomplish its purpose well, nor does it communicate effectively with the intended audience. The theme is not clear. The components appear to be "stuck on" or list-like. It is not clear that the student understands the core curriculum related to this project. Sources are not well referenced. The proper format is not used. The work contains errors, which interfere with the meaning.	
The work is extremely weak in most or all areas or has not been completed.	

Comments:

PERFORMANCE TASK ASSESSMENT LIST

Bulletin Board

Element	Assessment Points: Points Possible	Assessment Points: Earned Assessment — Self	Assessment Points: Earned Assessment — Teacher
1. The theme of the bulletin board is immediately evident.	______	______	______
2. Appropriate science concepts are stated accurately.	______	______	______
3. Adequate and accurate information supports the science concepts.	______	______	______
4. The display works visually. It is not too crowded. It appears organized, and it draws and holds the attention of the audience for which it was intended.	______	______	______
5. If there is a sequence to see, it is easy to follow.	______	______	______
6. Pictures, diagrams, graphs, and other visuals add to the interest and quality of information. They can be easily seen from several meters away.	______	______	______
7. Printed material is easy to read from a distance of several meters.	______	______	______
8. The bulletin board is neat and presentable.	______	______	______
Total	______	______	______

RUBRIC

Bulletin Board

	Rating
The student's bulletin board is very attractive. Not only is the science presented in a most accurate, interesting, and understandable way to the intended audience, it also is obvious that the student understands the science concepts.	
The student's bulletin board catches and holds the attention of the audience for which it was intended. The audience easily can study the display from several meters away. The information is appropriate to the task and shows that the student understands the basic science concepts.	
The student's bulletin board display is not interesting and/or attractive to the intended audience. The theme is unclear and/or the science presented is inaccurate or incomplete. Information is cluttered, unorganized, or too small to be studied from several meters away.	
The work is very poorly done or has not been completed.	

Comments:

PERFORMANCE TASK ASSESSMENT LIST

Cartoon/Comic Book

Element	Assessment Points: Points Possible	Assessment Points: Earned Assessment — Self	Assessment Points: Earned Assessment — Teacher
1. A character or characters has been created to portray important objects in the science lesson.	______	______	______
2. The characters are interesting and appropriate.	______	______	______
3. The science theme is appropriate to the assignment and is clearly evident.	______	______	______
4. The science concepts and supporting information are presented accurately through captions and dialogue.	______	______	______
5. The science concepts and supporting information are presented accurately through the drawings.	______	______	______
6. The artwork is creative and interesting.	______	______	______
7. The quality of the artwork is good.	______	______	______
8. The storyline supports the presentation of the science and is interesting to the intended audience.	______	______	______
9. The entire cartoon or comic book is appropriate, neat, and presentable.	______	______	______
Total	______	______	______

RUBRIC

Cartoon/Comic Book

	Rating
The student's cartoon or comic book is very well done. The central character(s) has been created in a most clever way to portray the central object(s) of this science lesson. The cartoon or comic book not only presents the science in a most accurate and interesting way, the artwork for the setting and the central character are extremely creative and are of excellent technical quality.	
The student's cartoon or comic book includes a very interesting character or characters that have been created to portray central objects in the science lesson. The story flows smoothly as the essential science concepts and supporting information are conveyed through visuals and the dialogue and/or captions. The artwork is of high technical quality. The work is appropriate and is presentable.	
The student's cartoon or comic book character is not very interesting. The science presented is not clear and/or is inaccurate. The story is weak and/or does not flow smoothly. The artwork is of poor technical quality. It is not neat, presentable, nor appropriate.	
The work is very poorly done or has not been completed.	

Comments:

PERFORMANCE TASK ASSESSMENT LIST

Display

Element	Assessment Points: Points Possible	Assessment Points: Earned Assessment — Self	Assessment Points: Earned Assessment — Teacher
1. The display has a clear theme that is appropriate to the concepts being conveyed.	______	______	______
2. The physical objects in the display are well coordinated with the theme.	______	______	______
3. Written descriptions clearly and accurately explain the science concepts.	______	______	______
4. The graphics such as symbols, words, statements, colors, patterns, and designs help carry out the theme.	______	______	______
5. There is a clear, creative, and thoughtful organization and coordination between the physical objects and the graphics in the display.	______	______	______
6. The display is attractive and presentable.	______	______	______
Total	______	______	______

RUBRIC

Display

	Rating
The student's display is eye-catching and immediately conveys a strong message. Written descriptions clearly and accurately explain the science concepts involved. The physical objects are particularly well-suited to the theme. The graphics are done with great artistic and technical skill. There is neither too much nor too little in the display.	
The student's theme for the display is very appropriate to the concepts being conveyed. The selection and arrangement of the physical objects are such that the theme is clearly carried out. Written descriptions accurately explain the science concepts involved. There is creative and thoughtful organization and coordination of the physical objects and the graphics. The display accomplishes its purpose with the intended audience.	
The student's theme is not very appropriate to the concepts being conveyed. The selection and organization of physical objects shows little thought or effort. Written descriptions are missing, or they do not clearly and accurately explain the science concepts involved. The display is not neat or presentable. The display does not accomplish its purpose with the intended audience.	
The work is very poorly done or has not been completed.	

Comments:

PERFORMANCE TASK ASSESSMENT LIST

Investigating an Issue Controversy

Element	Assessment Points: Points Possible	Earned Assessment: Self	Earned Assessment: Teacher
1. The alternative positions are stated clearly.	______	______	______
2. Criteria for choosing a position are stated. Criteria may be assigned values.	______	______	______
3. The audience was considered when making the list of criteria.	______	______	______
4. Each position was researched.	______	______	______
5. Support for each position is thoughtfully stated.	______	______	______
6. Information sources were evaluated regarding their degree of objectivity and accuracy.	______	______	______
7. Information from research is properly referenced.	______	______	______
8. Reasons for not supporting each position are stated thoughtfully.	______	______	______
9. If two or more people are involved in the issue controversy, each person in the group understands all reasons for and against each position.	______	______	______
10. If two or more people are involved in making the decision, an appropriate form of discussion, negotiation, and compromise is used.	______	______	______
11. The alternative positions are presented on each of the criteria.	______	______	______
12. A position is selected, and it is convincingly supported.	______	______	______
Total	______	______	______

RUBRIC

Investigating an Issue Controversy

	Rating
The students' positions are exceptionally well researched. A very thoughtful analysis is done for each position and a list of support for each position is prepared. The final decision is strongly and eloquently supported. If group work is involved, everyone understands the information completely for each position.	
The students clearly state the position in the controversy and make a thoughtful list of criteria to evaluate each position. Each position is researched, and a list of support for each position is prepared. The quality of the information sources is evaluated, and it is clear that the students selected both objective and accurate information. If two or more people are involved in the work, each understands the information for each position.	
The students' positions are not clearly or completely stated. The list of criteria to evaluate each position is incomplete and/or not fully appropriate. The positions are not explored adequately. The quality of the information used is not evaluated, is biased, or is unreliable. If two or more people are involved, decision-making strategies were not used.	
The work is very poorly done or has not been completed.	

Comments:

PERFORMANCE TASK ASSESSMENT LIST

Letter

Element	Assessment Points: Points Possible	Earned Assessment: Self	Earned Assessment: Teacher
1. Knowledge of the science concept is displayed through the facts and information used.	_____	_____	_____
2. Knowledge of the issue under debate is shown by the facts and information used.	_____	_____	_____
3. Balance is maintained (avoids extreme positions or overstatement).	_____	_____	_____
4. The letter anticipates and responds to the other side of the issue.	_____	_____	_____
5. Research goes beyond the scope of the classroom activities.	_____	_____	_____
6. The main idea is clearly stated.	_____	_____	_____
7. Supporting details and information appropriate to the main idea are accurate and forceful.	_____	_____	_____
8. References to sources of information are given for added emphasis and effect. References come from unbiased sources.	_____	_____	_____
9. The letter sounds rational and logical.	_____	_____	_____
10. The style of the letter is maintained.	_____	_____	_____
11. The letter is effective in getting the attention of the audience.	_____	_____	_____
12. There are no errors in writing.	_____	_____	_____
13. The letter is well organized.	_____	_____	_____
Total	_____	_____	_____

RUBRIC

Letter

	Rating
The student's editorial or letter meets all the requirements. In addition, the work is so well crafted that it could be published. The whole transcends the sum of the parts in producing a work that is as artful as it is scientific. The writer is able to gain the complete attention of the audience. The student provides insights into the problems that go beyond the material read and discussed in class. The paper is extremely well edited.	
The student's editorial or letter is well crafted. The student has demonstrated a thorough knowledge of the science behind the problem chosen as the focus of the writing. The writing is well organized around a central issue connected to the problem. Data is included to support ideas. The writer is able to gain the attention of the audience and is effective in establishing a position through the use of facts and logic. The paper is well edited with no more than one or two errors in the final draft.	
The student has not mastered or used one or more of the elements of a good editorial or letter. The work contains generalizations that are not supported. No attempt is made to give the science behind the issue. The student does not have a grasp of the issue nor a clear position to offer. There are multiple errors and flaws in organization.	
The editorial or letter is replete with errors, misinformation, or has not been completed.	

Comments:

PERFORMANCE TASK ASSESSMENT LIST

Newspaper Article

Element	Assessment Points: Points Possible	Earned Assessment: Self	Earned Assessment: Teacher
1. The general facts are correct.	______	______	______
2. The science facts are correct.	______	______	______
3. Quotes are accurate.	______	______	______
4. Quotes are used, but the whole story is not built on quotes.	______	______	______
5. There is a flow to the writing. It does not read like the minutes of a meeting.	______	______	______
6. The focus for the article is clearly evident in the first paragraph.	______	______	______
7. The readers report having their interest immediately captured.	______	______	______
8. The writing is concise. There is as much news as possible in the least amount of space.	______	______	______
9. There are enough supporting details for the story.	______	______	______
10. The article is written to communicate with the appropriate audience.	______	______	______
11. Humor is used in good taste.	______	______	______
12. The writer has been truthful.	______	______	______
13. The use of language is flawless.	______	______	______
14. The headline is both appropriate to the story and a "grabber."	______	______	______
15. Photographs clearly show what is intended.	______	______	______
16. The photographs are interesting and add information.	______	______	______
17. The caption for the picture is accurate and follows the correct format of left to right and top to bottom.	______	______	______
Total	______	______	______

RUBRIC

Newspaper Article

	Rating
The student's article is of exceptional quality. It conveys the story in a smooth and engaging style. The reader's interest is held throughout. Especially appropriate quotes and details are woven into the article. Photographs are highly informative and add much to the story; they show active rather than passive poses. The headline is memorable.	
The student's article is interesting and concise. The theme is immediately apparent, and the article flows smoothly as it is developed. Appropriate details support the theme. It is clear that the student knows the background science concepts. Photographs are clear and interesting. The headline is appropriate to the story and grabs the reader's attention.	
The student's article reads like the minutes of a meeting. It is not interesting. The theme is unclear and the article is not well organized. Details are missing or not appropriate. Science concepts are not used correctly. Photographs are not interesting and are of poor quality. The headline is not a grabber.	
The work is very poorly done or has not been completed.	

Comments:

PERFORMANCE TASK ASSESSMENT LIST

Oral Presentation

Element	Assessment Points: Points Possible	Earned Assessment: Self	Earned Assessment: Teacher
Content			
1. Science concepts are used accurately.	______	______	______
2. Accurate supporting details explain the concepts.	______	______	______
3. The vocabulary is appropriate to both the science content and the audience.	______	______	______
4. Visuals, including pictures, diagrams, photographs, videos, flow charts, and other props, are used appropriately to support the presentation.	______	______	______
5. There is a clear beginning, an organized body, and a clear conclusion.	______	______	______
Presentation			
6. Vocal qualities such as rate, volume, articulation, and enthusiasm are good.	______	______	______
7. Positive humor is used appropriately.	______	______	______
8. Body language such as eye contact, posture, and body movements are used effectively.	______	______	______
9. Attire is neat and presentable.	______	______	______
10. The speaker gives the audience time to think.	______	______	______
11. The speaker responds well to questions.	______	______	______
Total	______	______	______

RUBRIC

Oral Presentation

	Rating
The student makes an excellent presentation. He or she has masterful control of the science content and uses superb oral presentation skills. Strategies, such as visual aids, props, and/or humor, are especially effective. The audience is completely involved and has time to think about what is being said.	
The student clearly knows the subject. Science concepts are used correctly. Visual aids, which are interesting and clear, can be seen by everyone in the audience. The speaker is enthusiastic, can be easily heard by everyone, and uses eye contact and other body language to increase the effectiveness of the presentation. The audience is involved and has time to think about what is being said.	
The student does not have a strong command of the topic. Science concepts are not used well, and supporting details are lacking. Visual aids are poor or lacking. The talk is more like a reading than an oral presentation. Characteristics like volume, enthusiasm, and body language do not work for the student. The audience is not involved in the presentation.	
The work is very poorly done or has not been completed.	

Comments:

PERFORMANCE TASK ASSESSMENT LIST

Poster

Element	Assessment Points: Points Possible	Earned Assessment: Self	Earned Assessment: Teacher
1. The main theme is clear when you first look at it. A title helps to identify the theme.	______	______	______
2. Appropriate and accurate main ideas support the theme.	______	______	______
3. Appropriate and accurate details support the main ideas.	______	______	______
4. There is a wholeness about the poster. It does not seem like a collection of information.	______	______	______
5. The information in the poster is accurate and shows that the student thoroughly understands the science concepts.	______	______	______
6. Space, shapes, textures, and colors provide information and add to the overall effectiveness of the poster.	______	______	______
7. Pictures, photographs, drawings, diagrams, graphs, or other similar devices add to the overall effectiveness of the poster.	______	______	______
8. The format of the poster is appropriate to the task and to the audience for which it is intended.	______	______	______
9. The poster accomplishes its purpose with its intended audience.	______	______	______
10. The poster is very neat and presentable.	______	______	______
11. The poster is creative and interesting.	______	______	______
Total	______	______	______

RUBRIC

Poster

	Rating
The student's poster is outstanding, creative, and communicates information to the audience in an excellent manner. There are main ideas (the general) supported by appropriate details (the specific). Information is complete and accurate. All visuals add clarity and information. The work is very neat and presentable.	
The student's poster demonstrates a clear theme. There are main ideas supported by details. Information is complete. The concepts and information used show that the student understands the core curriculum related to the project. All visuals add clarity and information. The work is neat and presentable.	
The student's poster is difficult to understand even when its purpose is explained. The poster seems like a collection of pieces without a main idea to link them together. The student does not demonstrate a mastery of the core curriculum related to the project. Visuals are not used or are used inappropriately. The work is not neat and presentable.	
The work is very poorly done or has not been completed.	

Comments:

PERFORMANCE TASK ASSESSMENT LIST

Skit

Element	Assessment Points: Points Possible	Earned Assessment: Self	Earned Assessment: Teacher
1. The central theme of the skit presents a science concept that is appropriate to the assignment.	______	______	______
2. The science concept is presented accurately.	______	______	______
3. The actors and actresses have parts important to conveying the science concepts and information.	______	______	______
4. The storyline of the skit is interesting and helps to present the science information accurately.	______	______	______
5. The actions of each actor work well to help convey the science information accurately.	______	______	______
6. Props and/or costumes are well chosen, support the characters, and enhance the presentation of the science information.	______	______	______
7. Music and other sound effects support the storyline and also help to present the science information.	______	______	______
8. Dialogue supports the development of the characters, the storyline, and the presentation of the science information.	______	______	______
9. The skit was rehearsed sufficiently.	______	______	______
10. The audience could easily hear and see the skit.	______	______	______
11. The skit is entertaining to the audience.	______	______	______
	______	______	______
Total	______	______	______

RUBRIC

Skit

	Rating
The student's skit is wonderful. Dialogue is used to support the development of the characters and the presentation of science information. The skit shows that the student clearly understands the core curriculum related to the project.	
The student's skit has a central science theme that comes out clearly and accurately from the story. Dialogue is used for the development of the characters and the presentation of the science information. The skit is highly entertaining to its intended audience.	
The student's skit seems thrown together. Its science theme is unclear and/or developed inaccurately or poorly. The story is weak and unimaginative. It appears little thought or rehearsal went into the skit.	
The work is very poorly done or has not been completed.	

Comments:

PERFORMANCE TASK ASSESSMENT LIST

Slide Show or Photo Essay

Element	Assessment Points: Points Possible	Earned Assessment: Self	Earned Assessment: Teacher
1. Each picture in the set is composed well to clearly show what is intended.	______	______	______
2. Each picture is well focused and exposed appropriately.	______	______	______
3. The sequence of pictures has a clear theme.	______	______	______
4. The sequence is organized.	______	______	______
5. The set has its intended effect on the audience.	______	______	______
6. It is clear that the author understands the core concepts related to the topic and has chosen pictures appropriately.	______	______	______
7. Titles and other statements contribute to the theme and purpose of the set of pictures.	______	______	______
8. For the photo essay, the pictures are mounted and displayed in an attractive and effective manner.	______	______	______
Total	______	______	______

RUBRIC

Slide Show or Photo Essay

	Rating
The student's slide show or photo essay is highly organized and sequenced smoothly in an outstanding presentation of the theme. The technical quality of the pictures is excellent. The audience is powerfully affected by the pictures. It is clear that the student has an understanding of the core concepts of the theme. For the photo essay, the pictures are mounted and displayed in an attractive and very presentable manner.	
The student's slide show or photo essay offers a good presentation of the theme. The pictures clearly show what is intended. The photographs are organized, sequenced, and contain a clear theme. It is clear that the student has a basic understanding of the core concepts of the theme. For the photo essay, the pictures are mounted and displayed in an attractive and presentable manner.	
The student has taken pictures that do not clearly show what is intended. The set of pictures is not well organized. It is not clear that the student understands the core concepts. The pictures are not chosen so as to present the theme to the intended audience. For the photo essay, the pictures are not mounted and displayed in a presentable manner.	
The work is very poorly done or has not been completed.	

Comments:

PERFORMANCE TASK ASSESSMENT LIST

Song with Lyrics

Element	Points Possible	Earned Assessment: Self	Earned Assessment: Teacher
1. The main theme (melody) is clear and distinct.	______	______	______
2. If harmony is used, it supports and enhances the melody.	______	______	______
3. Any rhythmic element present is accurate.	______	______	______
4. The rhythmic element contributes to the song.	______	______	______
5. The lyrics contain a main theme.	______	______	______
6. Details in the lyrics support the main theme.	______	______	______
7. The lyrics convey accurate scientific information.	______	______	______
8. The song is appropriate for the intended audience.	______	______	______
9. The singer has practiced the song. The singer remembers the lyrics and melody.	______	______	______
10. The volume is reasonable.	______	______	______
11. The lyrics are communicated effectively through appropriate phrasing and dynamics.	______	______	______
Total	______	______	______

RUBRIC

Song with Lyrics

	Rating
The student's music and lyrics have a main theme and are outstanding and memorable. The lyrics convey very accurate scientific information. If rhythmic elements are used, they are accurate and contribute to the overall mood and style of the song. The song is appropriate for the intended audience.	
The student's song has a main theme in both the melody and lyrics. If rhythmic elements are used, they contribute to the overall mood and style of the song. The lyrics convey accurate scientific information. The song is appropriate for the intended audience.	
The student's melody and lyrics do not contain main themes. Any rhythmic elements used are offbeat and detract from the song. The scientific content of the lyrics is inaccurate. The music and lyrics do not work well together.	
The work is very poorly done or has not been completed.	

Performance	Rating
The student's singing is exceptional. It is clear that the student has worked to convey the scientific meaning through the phrasing and style of the song.	
The student's singing is successful. It is clear that the student has worked to convey the scientific meaning through the song. The song is well-received.	
The student's singing is poor. The meaning is not conveyed through the phrasing or style of the song.	
The work is very poorly done or has not been completed.	

Comments:

PERFORMANCE TASK ASSESSMENT LIST

Video

Element	Points Possible	Earned Assessment: Self	Earned Assessment: Teacher
1. The video has a clear science theme.	______	______	______
2. The video has a clear purpose such as to inform, persuade, or incite to action.	______	______	______
3. The science concepts are appropriate to the topic.	______	______	______
4. The information used to support the concepts is accurate.	______	______	______
5. The shots are appropriate to the theme.	______	______	______
6. The shots flow together and do not seem like a series of pieces.	______	______	______
7. Music, titles, and special effects, if used, strongly support the theme and purpose of the video and help connect the shots.	______	______	______
8. The sound of the video is of excellent quality.	______	______	______
9. The picture of the video is of excellent quality.	______	______	______
10. The video is creative and interesting.	______	______	______
11. The video achieves its purpose with the intended audience.	______	______	______
Total	______	______	______

RUBRIC

Video

	Rating
The student's video is incredibly effective in accomplishing its purpose with the intended audience. The science concepts and supporting information are superb. The video is creative, interesting, informative, and technically excellent.	
The student's video is a very good presentation of a science theme. The science concepts and supporting information are accurate. The video flows smoothly and the titles provide introductory and guiding information. The video is creative, interesting, and informative.	
The student's video has serious technical flaws. The video seems more like a series of pieces rather than a smooth story. The video does not accomplish its purpose with the intended audience.	
The work is very poorly done or has not been completed.	

Comments:

PERFORMANCE TASK ASSESSMENT LIST

Writer's Guide to Fiction

Element	Assessment Points: Points Possible	Earned Assessment: Self	Earned Assessment: Teacher
1. There is a clear theme to the story.	______	______	______
2. Science concepts in the story are accurate.	______	______	______
3. The plot centers around, develops, and resolves a problem.	______	______	______
4. The story has an engaging, interesting conflict that captures and holds the attention of the reader.	______	______	______
5. Each event or episode is important to the meaning of the plot.	______	______	______
6. The plot follows logically.	______	______	______
7. Details used are relevent and enrich the story.	______	______	______
8. The characters are consistent and believable.	______	______	______
9. The characters are developed through "showing" rather than "telling."	______	______	______
10. The story has a consistent point of view.	______	______	______
11. The setting is "shown" through believable details.	______	______	______
12. The setting enhances the story.	______	______	______
13. The title is appropriate, meaningful, and interesting.	______	______	______
14. The writing is correct.	______	______	______
15. The inspection of previous drafts shows that substantial revisions were made.	______	______	______
16. The work is neat and presentable.	______	______	______
Total	______	______	______

RUBRIC

Writer's Guide to Fiction

	Rating
The student's story is superior. It is unusually eloquent, complete, and creative. The plot creates and resolves a problem. The plot is logically sequenced. The story has a believable and detailed setting that includes the theme. There is evidence of substantial revision. The story is very neat and presentable.	
The student's story is excellent. The plot creates and resolves a problem. The plot is sequenced, and each event is important to the meaning of the story. The story has a believable setting that enhances the theme. There is evidence of revision. The story is neat and presentable.	
The student's story needs substantial improvement. Although there is a plot, it does not adequately create and/or resolve a problem. There are serious gaps in the plot and the events are not arranged in a clear and logical order. The setting is incomplete or not relevant to the plot. There is no clear theme, point, or message to the story. The writing is not neat or presentable.	
The work is very poorly done, does not have a plot, or has not been completed.	

Comments:

PERFORMANCE TASK ASSESSMENT LIST

Writer's Guide to Nonfiction

Element	Assessment Points: Points Possible	Earned Assessment: Self	Earned Assessment: Teacher
1. The introduction clearly states the thesis.	______	______	______
2. The introduction clearly introduces the main ideas.	______	______	______
3. The concepts used are appropriate and accurate.	______	______	______
4. Each paragraph has a topic sentence that is one of the main ideas.	______	______	______
5. Each paragraph has appropriate and accurate supporting details.	______	______	______
6. The conclusion sums up the points made in an interesting, thoughtful, and unique manner.	______	______	______
7. The writer's own voice and style are evident throughout the essay.	______	______	______
8. The title is clear and informative.	______	______	______
9. The writing is mechanically correct.	______	______	______
10. The writing is neat and presentable.	______	______	______
11. Visuals such as drawings, diagrams, or pictures are used in an appropriate way to add information and interest.	______	______	______
Total	______	______	______

RUBRIC

Writer's Guide to Nonfiction

	Rating
The student's writing is unusually insightful. It shows an exceptional grasp of the topic, task, audience, and purpose. Visuals are used to create interest and to give further information. The student's style is evident throughout the writing. The use of language is exemplary. The writing is neat and presentable.	
The student's writing is excellent. It is clear that the student understood the task, audience, and purpose of the writing. The concepts used are appropriate and accurate. The student's style is felt throughout the writing. Visuals are used to add information. The writing is mechanically correct and neatly presented.	
The student's writing needs improvement. Although the student attempts to complete the task as given, it is not entirely clear that he/she fully understood the task, audience, or purpose of the writing. The student remains focused on a single topic or thesis throughout much of the piece, but he/she has difficulty verbalizing his/her thesis. Supporting details may be inappropriate or inaccurate. It is not clear that the student used his/her own style or voice. There are numerous mechanical errors, and the work is not neat and presentable.	
The student's writing is very poor, showing little attempt to complete the task given. There is an overall lack of focus, elaboration, organization, or the work has not been completed.	

Comments:

PERFORMANCE TASK ASSESSMENT LIST
Writing in Science

Element	Assessment Points: Points Possible	Earned Assessment: Self	Earned Assessment: Teacher
1. Concepts are used correctly.	______	______	______
2. Concepts are supported with accurate details.	______	______	______
3. The student uses appropriate information in the writing.	______	______	______
4. If needed, visuals such as drawings or diagrams are appropriately used and they support the writing.	______	______	______
5. Higher-order thinking such as association, integration, synthesis, analysis, and/or evaluation is evident.	______	______	______
6. Appropriate vocabulary, language mechanics, and complete sentences are used.	______	______	______
7. References, if needed, are properly made.	______	______	______
8. The writing is organized and focused.	______	______	______
9. The purpose of the writing is clearly carried out.	______	______	______
10. The writing is neat and presentable.	______	______	______
Total	______	______	______

RUBRIC

Writing in Science

	Rating
The student's writing is excellent. Higher-order thinking is clearly evident. The information is presented in an especially insightful manner. The sequence of ideas is thoughtful and well organized. The thoughtful mastery of language, complete sentences, spelling, and grammar is quite evident. The writing is very neat and presentable.	
The student uses appropriate concepts accurately and supports the writing with details. Science vocabulary is appropriate to both the topic and the audience. The sequence of ideas is thoughtful and organized. The thoughtful use of language, including complete sentences, spelling, and language mechanics, is evident. The writing is neat and presentable.	
The student's writing is not focused and organized. Concepts are missing or incorrectly used. Science vocabulary is not well selected. Language mechanics are poor. The work is not neat or presentable.	
The work is very poorly done or has not been completed.	

Comments:

PERFORMANCE TASK ASSESSMENT LIST

Concept Map

Element	Assessment Points: Points Possible	Earned Assessment: Self	Earned Assessment: Teacher
1. The set of concept words in the ovals is appropriate to the science topic.	_____	_____	_____
2. The set of concept words is organized from most general to most specific.	_____	_____	_____
3. There is an appropriate number of levels of this hierarchy (general to specific) of concept words.	_____	_____	_____
4. The linking words (on the lines) used to connect concept words are appropriate to the relationships being made between those concept words.	_____	_____	_____
5. Valid cross-links are made between concept words in different parts of the concept map.	_____	_____	_____
6. The linking words (on the lines) used to make the cross-links are appropriate to the relationships being made between the concept words.	_____	_____	_____
7. The concept map has an appropriate title.	_____	_____	_____
8. The concept map is easy to follow.	_____	_____	_____
9. Prior knowledge and new knowledge are indicated.	_____	_____	_____
10. The concept map is neat and presentable.	_____	_____	_____
Total	_____	_____	_____

RUBRIC

Concept Map

	Rating
The student's concept map is excellent and completely and thoughtfully organizes and connects the concepts. There are more levels to the concept hierarchy than in a good concept map, and there are some especially insightful cross-links. The student has been very clear about which parts of the concept map represent his/her new learning. The map is very easy to follow and is neat and presentable.	
The student selects an appropriate set of concept words to include in the concept map. These concept words are arranged in a hierarchy from most general to most specific. There are several levels of this hierarchy. There are cross-links between concept words in different parts of the hierarchy. The student has indicated which parts of the concept map represent his/her new learning. The map is easy to follow and is neat and presentable.	
The student uses some concept words inappropriately. Some important concept words are missing in the map. The hierarchy of the list of concept words has only a few levels. While some connections are made correctly, the linking words used to show connections between concept words indicate incorrect connections. There are few, if any, cross-links. The concept map is not easy to follow, and it is not neat and presentable.	
The work is very poorly done or has not been completed.	

Comments:

PERFORMANCE TASK ASSESSMENT LIST
Events Chain

Element	Assessment Points: Points Possible	Earned Assessment: Self	Earned Assessment: Teacher
Items in an Events Chain			
1. The items included are accurate.	______	______	______
2. The collection of items shows thoughtful selection of the most important elements.	______	______	______
3. Each item is stated clearly.	______	______	______
4. The sequence is logical.	______	______	______
5. The title catches your attention and accurately prepares you for the information in the chart.	______	______	______
6. Geometric forms, colors, textures, arrows, and other techniques add meaning and clarity to the events chain.	______	______	______
7. The events chain is neat and presentable. It is not overcrowded, nor is it too sparse.	______	______	______
8. The events chain communicates well with its intended audience.	______	______	______
The Written Explanation of Each Element of the Events Chain			
9. The main idea is stated clearly.	______	______	______
10. Sufficient supporting details explain the main idea.	______	______	______
11. Language is used correctly.	______	______	______
12. The writing is neat, presentable, and concise.	______	______	______
Total	______	______	______

RUBRIC

Events Chain

	Rating
The student's events chain is remarkable in how clearly and completely it communicates its purpose to its intended audience. The collection of elements is selected thoughtfully. The title attracts attention and accurately conveys the content of the chain. Visuals superbly add meaning and clarity to the event chain. Overall, it is very attractive, neat, and presentable.	
The student uses all the elements of the chain accurately for the processes and information they represent. The collection of elements is selected to accomplish its purpose for the intended audience. The title attracts attention and conveys the content of the events chain. Visuals add meaning and clarity to the chain. The effect is attractive, neat, and presentable.	
The student's events chain has inaccuracies in the information and/or processes presented. The events chain is difficult to follow because of problems, such as overcrowding or missing or misplaced elements. Visuals are not used well. The events chain does not convey its intended message to its audience. It is seriously lacking in organization and neatness.	
The work is very poorly done or has not been completed.	

Comments:

PERFORMANCE TASK ASSESSMENT LIST
Idea Organizer

Element	Assessment Points: Points Possible	Assessment Points: Earned Assessment: Self	Assessment Points: Earned Assessment: Teacher
1. Geometric figures are used. There is a large central figure and other shapes surrounding it.	______	______	______
2. Geometric shapes are used throughout the web to convey relationships between elements in the web.	______	______	______
3. The topic and main ideas are clear.	______	______	______
4. The topic is listed in the central figure, and main ideas connected to the topic are placed in surrounding figures.	______	______	______
5. An appropriate number of details support each main idea.	______	______	______
6. Enough information has been included to indicate that the concepts are understood.	______	______	______
7. The information is accurate.	______	______	______
8. Space, shapes, textures, and colors provide information and add to the overall effectiveness of the organizer.	______	______	______
9. Pictures, drawings, designs, and other graphics provide information and add to the overall effectiveness of the organizer.	______	______	______
10. The organizer is neat, clear, and presentable.	______	______	______
Total	______	______	______

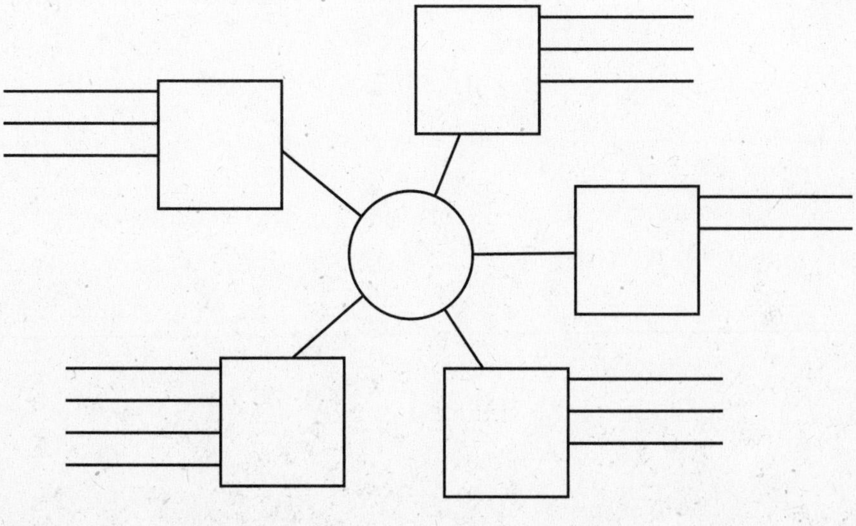

RUBRIC

Idea Organizer

	Rating
The student's organizer is outstanding. The appropriate geometric figures display the main topic, ideas, and details clearly. The details for each qualifier support the main ideas effectively. Visuals add clarity and information. The organizer is very clear, neat, and presentable.	
The topic and main ideas of the student's organizer are very clear when you first look at it. The geometric figures display the main topic, ideas, and details clearly. The details for each qualifier support the main ideas. The concepts and information used show that the student understands the assignment. The organizer is clear, neat and presentable.	
The student's organizer is difficult to understand. It seems either overcrowded or sparse. The main ideas do not seem to connect to the topic or are not similar in value. Some information is incomplete or inaccurate. There are no visuals. The work is not clear, neat, or presentable. There are many mechanical flaws.	
The work is very poorly done or has not been completed.	

Comments:

PERFORMANCE TASK ASSESSMENT LIST

Venn Diagram and Pro/Con Issue

Element	Assessment Points: Points Possible	Earned Assessment: Self	Earned Assessment: Teacher
1. The two objects or events to be compared are stated clearly.	______	______	______
2. A thoughtful list of characteristics unique and important to object or event number 1 is made. Appropriate and accurate information has been used to make this list.	______	______	______
3. A thoughtful list of characteristics unique and important to object or event number 2 is made. Appropriate and accurate information has been used to make this list.	______	______	______
4. The characteristics chosen to contrast the two objects or events show a clear understanding of the science involved.	______	______	______
5. A list of important characteristics common to both objects or events is made. Appropriate and accurate information has been used to make this list.	______	______	______
6. The common set of characteristics chosen shows a clear understanding of the science involved.	______	______	______
7. There is a priority order within the lists that shows an understanding of what is important to the task at hand.	______	______	______
8. The Venn diagram is neat and presentable.	______	______	______
Total	______	______	______

Note: This Performance Task Assessment List for a Venn diagram can be adapted for use as a Pro/Con Graphic Organizer

RUBRIC

Venn Diagram and Pro/Con Issue

	Rating
The student's selection and statement of the characteristics that distinguish and identify commonalities of the two objects (or events) are done thoughtfully. The overall concept of science being studied is clear. There is a priority order within the lists that demonstrates a very strong understanding of the science involved.	
The student has shown that he/she understands the science by selecting a set of unique characteristics for each object (or event). A set of characteristics common to the objects (or events) reveals a strong understanding of the science content. The Venn diagram is neat and presentable.	
The characteristics chosen by the student to compare and contrast the objects (or events) shows little understanding of the important science concepts. The lists seem unorganized and/or random.	
The work is very poorly done or has not been completed.	

Comments:

PERFORMANCE TASK ASSESSMENT LIST

Group Work

Element	Assessment Points: Points Possible	Earned Assessment: Self	Earned Assessment: Teacher
1. Student comes to the group prepared for the group work.	______	______	______
2. All individual tasks for the group are completed on time and with quality.	______	______	______
3. Student participates in a constructive manner.	______	______	______
4. Student encourages others to participate in a constructive manner.	______	______	______
5. Student is a good, active listener.	______	______	______
6. Positions are supported in a strong and thoughtful manner.	______	______	______
7. Student disagrees in an agreeable manner.	______	______	______
8. Student can reach compromises.	______	______	______
9. Responsibility is shared in helping the group get the job done on time and according to directions.	______	______	______
10. Positive human relations are promoted in the group.	______	______	______
Total	______	______	______

RUBRIC

Group Work

	Rating
The student's group work skills are very highly developed. The student shows responsibility by being well prepared. The student contributes during discussions and actively listens to others. The student strongly supports his/her own opinions. The student promotes positive human relations within the group.	
The student shows responsibility by being prepared for group work and completing all individual tasks on time and with quality. The student listens to others and is tolerant of divergent views. The student supports his/her own opinions and works with the group to carry out a plan to accomplish the group's goal on time and with quality. The student promotes favorable human relations within the group.	
The student is not prepared for group work and does not complete individual tasks on time and/or with quality. The student contributes too little or excessively dominates group work. The student may not support his/her own position or may not be willing to listen to others. The student is a poor team player and does not work to develop and carry out a plan to accomplish a task. The student does not promote positive human relations in the group.	
The student is a very poor group worker or will not participate at all.	

Comments:

PERFORMANCE TASK ASSESSMENT LIST

Making a Performance Assessment Task

Element	Points Possible	Earned Assessment: Self	Earned Assessment: Teacher
1. The concepts being assessed are important.	_____	_____	_____
2. The process skills being assessed are important.	_____	_____	_____
3. The background statement is friendly and gives an interesting context for the task.	_____	_____	_____
4. The statement of the task describes the type of product(s) to make. The product is authentic in that it is like one occurring in the larger world.	_____	_____	_____
5. When the product is such that reasoning would not be evidently clear, some preliminary work, such as a graphic organizer, is part of the required task.	_____	_____	_____
6. There are Performance Task Assessment Lists for the processes and products of this task. These lists are written in appropriate detail.	_____	_____	_____
7. Self-assessment is an important part of the task.	_____	_____	_____
8. A specific audience for the product has been identified. The audience would have a real interest in the product.	_____	_____	_____
9. The purpose of the task describes what the product is intended to accomplish for the student and/or for the audience of this product.	_____	_____	_____
10. The procedure provides appropriate structure to this task.	_____	_____	_____
11. In the process, there is access to materials and information in a way similar to the way such materials and information are available to problem solvers in the larger world.	_____	_____	_____
12. Reasonable time is allocated to the task.	_____	_____	_____
13. Safety issues are properly addressed.	_____	_____	_____
Total	_____	_____	_____

RUBRIC

Making a Performance Assessment Task

	Rating
The performance task is excellent in how well it engages the student in a thoughtful, active project that absolutely requires the use of important concepts, process skills, and work habits from the curricula. It is clear that the assessor will be able to get a very good picture of the student's competencies. The task is authentic because the student's products and/or performances and the processes being used are like those occurring in the larger world.	
The concepts, process skills, and work habits of the student being assessed are important. The task clearly defines the type of product or performance to be crafted. The purpose of the task clearly states what the product is intended to accomplish with the intended audience. The procedure is listed in appropriate detail and may include reference to the performance task assessment lists the student should use. Safety is addressed, and time and materials are available.	
It is not clear that this task will allow the assessor to get a clear picture of how well the student can use concepts, process skills, and work habits intended to be assessed. The products of the task are not well defined, and/or the audience is not well described. The procedure is not at the correct level of specificity for these students. Safety is not adequately addressed and materials are not appropriate.	
The task is very poorly constructed and will not work or has not been completed.	

Comments:

PERFORMANCE TASK ASSESSMENT LIST

Management Plan

Element	Points Possible	Earned Assessment: Self	Earned Assessment: Teacher
1. The heading is completed properly.	______	______	______
2. The list of tasks is complete.	______	______	______
3. The tasks are specific.	______	______	______
4. The target dates for completion of each task are appropriate.	______	______	______
5. Thoughtful consideration has gone into a description of the barriers to successfully completing the project.	______	______	______
6. Thoughtful consideration has gone into a description of strategies for overcoming those barriers.	______	______	______
7. The plan is neat and presentable.	______	______	______
Total	______	______	______

RUBRIC

Management Plan

	Rating
The student's management plan is highly organized and detailed. Barriers are especially well defined, and action plans to avoid them are clearly workable. It is very clear that the student has completely thought about the project, because the elements are listed in proper order and with complete details.	
The student's management plan is very organized and complete. The elements listed are in order and are of sufficient detail. The student has thoughtfully considered potential barriers and has planned to surmount each. The plan is neat.	
The student's management plan is incomplete. Elements are missing and/or are not specific. Elements may be listed in an incorrect order. Barriers have not been identified, and/or the student has not thought about how to surmount them. The plan is not prepared neatly.	
The work is very poorly done or has not been completed.	

Comments:

PERFORMANCE TASK ASSESSMENT LIST

Science Journal

Element	Assessment Points: Points Possible	Assessment Points: Earned Assessment — Self	Assessment Points: Earned Assessment — Teacher
1. The student's name is listed.	______	______	______
2. All entries are dated.	______	______	______
3. Many science concepts are explored.	______	______	______
4. Diagrams, sketches, and drawings indicate logical thought.	______	______	______
5. Observations are organized and written in complete sentences.	______	______	______
6. Questions show higher-order thinking such as analysis, synthesis, and evaluation.	______	______	______
7. "What if. . .?" statements show that relevant and interesting independent and dependent variables are being considered.	______	______	______
8. Sketches of inventions and models show understanding of science concepts.	______	______	______
9. Graphic organizers are used to organize thinking.	______	______	______
10. Problems and concerns are identified, and ideas are provided for their solution.	______	______	______
11. Interesting and enjoyable elements are identified and reasons given for them.	______	______	______
12. Exploration as a learner is evident.	______	______	______
13. Goals to improve study habits have been set.	______	______	______
14. Lists of interesting information and ideas from sources, such as newspapers, magazines, and television, are included.	______	______	______
Total	______	______	______

RUBRIC

Science Journal

	Rating
The student's science journal shows that he/she has very thoughtfully considered many elements of science and has tackled some very tough concepts. Unanswered questions are revisited as more and more complete answers are constructed. It is clear that the student is able to look inside to see himself/herself as a learner, finding and solving problems, and striving to improve work habits.	
The student's science journal is very organized and complete. Many science concepts appear in it, and it is clear that the student has spent much time and hard work to explore ideas and phenomena through graphics and in writing. Good, clear thinking is found throughout. The student has shown some ability to explore how he or she goes about learning and has set and followed some goals for improvement.	
The student's science journal is incomplete. It shows little effort to be complete or detailed. Little higher-order thinking is evident. There also is little evidence that the student understands himself/herself as a learner. Strengths and weaknesses have not been explored well.	
The student's science journal is very incomplete and unorganized or has not been completed.	

Comments:

PERFORMANCE TASK ASSESSMENT LIST

Science Portfolio

Element	Points Possible	Assessment Points Earned: Self	Assessment Points Earned: Teacher
Categories for the Contents of the Portfolio			
1. Range of thinking and creativity in science: the collection of items shows off thinking skills and creativity in science.	_____	_____	_____
2. Use of the scientific process: the collection of items shows understanding of the scientific process.	_____	_____	_____
3. Models and inventions: the collection of items shows quality models and inventions.	_____	_____	_____
4. Connections between science and other subjects: the collection of items demonstrates thoughtful connections made between science and other school subjects.	_____	_____	_____
5. Reading or viewing related to science: the collection of items shows that student regularly read or viewed materials related to science.	_____	_____	_____
6. Other: the collection of items demonstrates skill in this area.	_____	_____	_____
The Portfolio as a Whole			
7. The collection of items in each category shows a wide range of work.	_____	_____	_____
8. The index for each category is clear.	_____	_____	_____
9. The self-reflective narrative in each category addresses strengths and weaknesses in that area.	_____	_____	_____
10. The self-reflective narrative in each category tells how improvement was made in the area for that category.	_____	_____	_____
11. The self-reflective narrative in each category tells about plans for further development in that area.	_____	_____	_____
12. The portfolio has a clearly labeled cover including the student's and teacher's names.	_____	_____	_____
13. The portfolio contains a collection of items, an index, and a self-reflective narrative for each category.	_____	_____	_____
14. The portfolio shows an understanding of the concepts, skills, and work habits important to the class.	_____	_____	_____
Total	_____	_____	_____

RUBRIC

Science Portfolio

	Rating
The student's science portfolio works as a whole to show a masterful control of the concepts, information, skills, and work habits important to the science class. A wide range of high quality products demonstrate that the student has a very high level of understanding of his/her own science literacy and is setting highly challenging personal goals for learning. The index does an excellent job of guiding the reader through the items in each category. The self-reflective narratives are masterfully focused on the individual's learning process and work habits.	
The student's science portfolio has a collection for each of the five categories. Not only does each collection show excellent work, but the collection works as a whole to show a well-rounded exhibition in that category. The index does a clear job of guiding the reader though the items in each category. The self-reflective narrative shows thoughtful insight into the student's strengths and any weakness, areas of growth, and goals for further growth.	
The student's collections for each category show little quality work. The collections are very limited. Some categories may be missing. The index may be unorganized, incomplete, or unclear. The self-reflective narratives show that the student has very little honest insight into his/her strengths and weaknesses. Learning goals are missing or show little thought.	
The student's portfolio is very poorly done. It is unorganized and incomplete. Little, if any, good work is evident. Self-reflective narratives, if present, show very little insight or the portfolio has not been completed.	

Comments:

Rubric Scoring Systems

In This Section

The rubrics in the previous section have an open column under the *Rating* head to allow you to customize your scoring or ranking based on your particular needs or your students' needs.

Scores or ranks can be expressed as words, letters, numbers, or with symbols. Below are some suggestions:

Words:

- Excellent - Quality - Acceptable - Unacceptable
- Demonstrates high proficiency - Clearly demonstrates proficiency - Demonstrates progress toward proficiency - Demonstrates strong need for proficiency
- Exceeds expectations - Meets expectations - Approaching expectations - Below expectations
- Exemplary - Proficient - Marginal - Beginning
- Distinguished - Competent - Developing - Inadequate

Numbers:

- 4 (highest)   3   2   1/0 (lowest)
- 10-9 (highest)   8, 7, 6   5, 4, 3   2, 1, 0 (lowest)
- 100 percent   85 percent   75 percent   60 percent or lower

Letters:

- A (highest)   B   C   D/F (lowest)
- if you want to avoid using customary letter grades (A, B, C, D, F) choose another series of letters, such as W-X-Y-Z.

Sample Rubrics and Checklists

In addition to the rubrics and checklists presented in the last section of this booklet, samples of other types of assessment lists follow on pages 89 to 178. These samples can be used to customize individual or group assessment in your classroom.

Classification Assessment	4	3	2	1
Selection of items	I selected important and interesting items to classify. They may be difficult to classify.	I selected items that are fairly important and that made me think when I classified them.	I selected items that were not very important or that were simple to put into categories.	I selected items that were unimportant or that had nothing to do with the classification.
Creation of categories	I created categories that were meaningful and important to the items being classified. My category names were complete and well-written.	I created categories that made me think about the important characteristics of the items. Most category names are fairly complete and well-written.	I created categories that do not reflect the very important characteristics of the items. Many category names are too vague or are poorly written.	I created categories that used only unimportant characteristics of the items. Most category names are vague or poorly witten.
Placement of items	I placed all 10 items into logical categories.	I placed at least 8 of 10 items into logical categories.	I placed at least 6 of 10 items into logical categories.	I placed 5 or fewer items into logical categories.
Written explanations	I clearly and completely described how and why I selected the 10 items. I also discussed some of the difficulties I faced in classifying them.	I described how I selected the items. I attempted to discuss some of the difficulties I faced in classifying them.	I described how I selected the items, but the description is incomplete or confusing.	My explanations are incomplete or very confusing.
Mechanics of writing	My written work is legible and follows standard writing conventions (punctuation, capitalization, spelling, and grammar).	My writing errors are few and do not interfere with the communication and understanding of concepts.	I made several errors that distract from the communication and understanding of concepts.	I made many errors that interfere with the communication and understanding of concepts.

Scientific Method	**4**	**3**	**2**	**1**
Question for investigation	Appropriate and fully stated in correct terms	Appropriate and fairly well-written	Somewhat workable, is poorly stated, or is incomplete	Unclear or unworkable
Hypothesis	Well-written, fully-stated in clear terms with a good explanation or justification	Acceptable; justification or explanation is good	Weak or unclear; no explanation or justification is given	Illogical or does not apply to the investigation
Investigation plan	Very good; fully explained; includes steps, materials, and variables; easy to understand what the student did and how it was done	Good; workable; most of the steps, materials, and variables are included	Sketchy; somewhat workable; important steps, materials, and variables are not included	No steps listed or is totally unworkable
Data collection and organization	Recorded and organized into charts, graphs, sketches, etc. that are complete and easy to read; results are well-summarized in a written statement	Recorded and organized well; results are summarized	Partially recorded and/or organized ineffectively; results are not summarized	Not recorded in an acceptable manner; not organized in any way
Conclusions	Logical and well-stated with a good comparison of results to the original hypothesis; clearly the student learned something	Fairly well-stated with acceptable comparisons between results and hypothesis	Present and fairly logical, but not explained well; no comparison of results with hypothesis	Totally illogical or not supported by the investigation
Mechanics of writing	Work is legible and in final copy form; follows writing conventions (punctuation, capitalization, spelling, and grammar)	Errors are few and do not interfere with the communication and understanding of concepts	Several errors are made that interfere with the communication and understanding of concepts	Multiple errors are made that interfere with the communication and understanding of concepts

Self Assessment

Name ______________________________ Date ______________

1. New science concepts or facts I have recently learned are ______________________________

2. Topics causing me difficulty at this time are ______________________________

3. My feelings about science at this time are ______________________________

4. The progress I have made in science over the past few weeks involves ______________________________

5. The topics that interest me, which I would like to study further are ______________________________

6. To improve our science class we should try ______________________________

Journal Assessment Checklist

______ detailed observations

______ questions students would like to be able to answer and possible answers to those questions

______ labeled drawings and sketches with comments

______ What if . . . . ? questions

______ sketches and notes about models and inventions

______ notes about interesting science items from newspapers, magazines, and other media

______ thoughts about what is interesting and enjoyable about science class

______ thoughts about difficulties in learning science and how to overcome the difficulties

______ writing skills improving

______ communication skills improving

______ showing a relationship between science and the real world

Group Cooperation Checklist	Excellent	Good	Fair	Poor
Stayed on task				
Worked together/ cooperated				
Handled materials well/ cleaned up				
Completed the task				

Note: Put a checkmark or write an explanation in the appropriate box.

Reports and Presentations				
	Scientific thought	Oral presentation	Exhibit display	Written report
4				
3				
2				
1				

Category	Criteria	Rating

Note: Use a number or letter in the ratings box.

Areas to Evaluate	20	15	10	5	1

Bibliography

1. Airasian, P.W. (1991). *Classroom Assessment.* New York: McGraw-Hill, Inc.
2. American Association for the Advancement of Science (1989). *Project 2061: Science for All Americans.* Washington, D.C.: American Association for the Advancement of Science.
3. Arter, J., and Spandel, V. (1992). "Using Portfolios of Student Work in Instruction and Assessment." *Educational Measurement: Issues and Practice,* 11, 1:36-44.
4. Barnes, Lehman W. and Marianne B. Barnes (1991). "Assessment, Practically Speaking. How Can We Measure Hands-on Science Skills?" *Science and Children,* 28, 6:14-15.
5. Carin, Arthur A. (1993). *Teaching Science Through Discovery.* New York: Merrill.
6. Champagne, A.B., Lovitts, B.E. and Clinger, B.J. (1990). *Assessment in the Service of Science.* Washington, D.C.: American Association for the Advancement of Science.
7. "From Teachers Who Know: Assessment for Maximum Teaching and Learning (1999)." *OASCD Journal,* Spring: 7-12.
8. Gronlund, N.E. (1993). *How to Make Achievement Tests and Assessments.* Boston, MA: Allyn and Bacon.
9. Ham, Mary and Dennis Adams (1991). "Portfolio Assessment. It's Not Just for Artists Anymore." *The Science Teacher,* 58, 1:18.
10. Kulm, G. and Malcom, S.M. (1991). *Science Assessment in the Service of Reform.* Washington, D.C.: American Association for the Advancement of Science.
11. National Research Council. (1992). *National Science Education Standards: A Sampler.* Washington, D.C.: National Research Council.
12. *National Science Education Standards.* (1996). National Academy of Sciences, Washington, D.C.: National Academy Press. 78-100.
13. North Central Regional Educational Laboratory. (2000). *//ncrel. org*
14. Raizen, Senta A. et al. (1989). *Assessment in Elementary Science Education.* Colorado Springs, CO: The National Center for Improving Science Education.
15. Stiggins, R.J. (1987). "Design and Development of Performance Assessments." *Educational Measurement: Issues and Practice.* 6,3:33-42.
16. Vermont Department of Education. (1992). *Looking Beyond "The Answer:" The Report of Vermont's Mathematics Portfolio Assessment Program, Pilot Year 1990-1991.* Montpelier: Department of Education.
17. Wangsatorntanakhun, Jo Anne. (1999). *Designing Performance Assessment: Challenges for the Three-Story Intellect.* Ruamrudee International School: 1-2.
18. Wiggins, G. (1989). "A True Test: Toward More Authentic and Equitable Assessment." *Phi Delta Kappan,* 70, 9: 703-713.